# FM 21-31

## US ARMY FIELD MANUAL

# TOPOGRAPHIC

# SYMBOLS

## 1952

### CIVILIAN REFERENCE EDITION

UNABRIDGED HANDBOOK ON OVER 200 SYMBOLS FOR MAP READING
AND LAND NAVIGATION FROM USGS QUADRANGLE MAPS

U.S. DEPARTMENT OF THE ARMY

Doublebit Press

# The Military Outdoors Skills Series
## Historic Field Manuals and Military Guides
## on Outdoors Skills and Travel

Military manuals contain essential knowledge about outdoors life, thriving while in the field, and self-sufficiency. Unfortunately, many great military books, field manuals, and technical guides over the years have become less available and harder to find. These have either been rescinded by the armed forces or are otherwise out of print due to their age. This does not mean that these manuals are worthless or "out of date" – in fact, the opposite is true! It is true that the US Military frequently updates its manuals as its protocols frequently change based on the current times and combat situations that our armed services face. However, the knowledge about the outdoors over the entire history of military publications is timeless!

By publishing the **Military Outdoors Skills Series**, it is our goal at Doublebit Press to do what we can to preserve and share valuable military works that hold timeless knowledge about outdoors life, navigation, and survival. These books include official unrestricted texts such as army field manuals (the FM series), technical manuals (the TM series), and other military books from the Air Force, Navy, and texts from before 1900. Through remastered reprint editions of military handbooks and field manuals, outdoors enthusiasts, bushcrafters, hunters, scouts, campers, survivalists, nature lore experts, and military historians can preserve the time-tested skills and institutional knowledge that was learned through hard lessons and training by the U.S. Military and our expert soldiers.

Soldiers were the original campers and survivalists! Because of this, military field manuals about outdoors life contain essential knowledge about thriving in the wilds. This book is not just for soldiers!

This book is an important contribution to outdoors literature and has important historical and collector value toward preserving the American outdoors tradition. The knowledge it holds is an invaluable reference for practicing skills related to thriving in the outdoors. Its chapters thoroughly discuss some of the essential building blocks of outdoors knowledge that are fundamental but may have been forgotten as equipment gets fancier and technology gets smarter. In short, this book was chosen for Historic Edition printing because much of the basic skills and knowledge it contains could be forgotten or put to the wayside in trade for more modern conveniences and methods.

Although the editors at Doublebit Press are thrilled to have comfortable experiences in the woods and love our high-tech and light-weight equipment, we are also realizing that the basic skills taught by the old experts are more essential than ever as our culture becomes more and more hooked on digital technology. We don't want to risk forgetting the important steps, skills, or building blocks involved with thriving in the outdoors. This Civilian Reference Edition reprint represents a collection of military handbooks and field manuals that are essential contributions to the American outdoors tradition despite originating with the military. In the most basic sense, these books are the collection of experiences by the great experts of outdoors life: our countless expert soldiers who learned to thrive in the backwoods, deserts, extreme cold environments, and jungles of the world.

With technology playing a major role in everyday life, sometimes we need to take a step back in time to find those basic building blocks used for gaining mastery – the things that we have luckily not completely lost and has been recorded in books over the last two centuries. These skills aren't forgotten, they've just been shelved. *It's time to unshelve them once again and reclaim the lost knowledge of self-sufficiency.*

Based on this commitment to preserving our outdoors heritage, we have taken great pride in publishing this book as a complete original work. We hope it is worthy of both study and collection by outdoors folk in the modern era of outdoors and traditional skills life.

Unlike many other photocopy reproductions of classic books that are common on the market, this Historic Edition does not simply place poor photography of old texts on our pages and use error-prone optical scanning or computer-generated text. We want our work to speak for itself, and reflect the quality demanded by our customers who spend their hard-earned money. With this in mind, each Historic Edition book that has been chosen for publication is carefully remastered from original print books, *with the Doublebit Civilian Reference Edition printed and laid out in the exact way that it was presented at its original publication.* We provide a beautiful, memorable experience that is as true to the original text as best as possible, but with the aid of modern technology to make as beautiful a reading experience as possible for books that are typically over a century old. Military historians and outdoors enthusiasts alike are sure to appreciate the care to preserve this work!

Because of its age and because it is presented in its original form, the book may contain misspellings, inking errors, and other print blemishes that were common for the age. However, these are exactly the things that we feel give the book its character, which we preserved in this Historic Edition. During digitization, we ensured that each illustration in the text was clean and sharp with the least amount of loss from being copied and digitized as possible. Full-page plate illustrations are presented as they were found, often including the extra blank page that was often behind a plate. For the covers, we use the original cover design to give the book its original feel. We are sure you'll appreciate the fine touches and attention to detail that your Historic Edition has to offer.

For outdoors and military history enthusiasts who demand the best from their equipment, the Doublebit Press Civilian Reference Edition reprint of this military manual was made with you in mind. Both important and minor details have equally both been accounted for by our publishing staff, down to the cover, font, layout, and images. It is the goal of Doublebit Civilian Reference Edition series to preserve outdoors heritage, but also be cherished as collectible pieces, worthy of collection in any outdoorsperson's library and that can be passed to future generations.

DEPARTMENT OF THE ARMY FIELD MANUAL

FM 21-31

This manual, together with FM 21-30, 28 June 1951, supersedes FM 21-30, 15 October 1943, including C 1, 21 April 1944, C 2, 15 February 1945, and C 3, 28 February 1945

# TOPOGRAPHIC
# SYMBOLS

DEPARTMENT OF THE ARMY   •   JANUARY 1952

United States Government Printing Office
Washington : 1952

DEPARTMENT OF THE ARMY
WASHINGTON 25, D. C., *4 January 1952*

FM 21–31 is published for the information and guidance of all concerned.

[AG 061.01 (16 Oct 51)]

BY ORDER OF THE SECRETARY OF THE ARMY:


OFFICIAL:
WM. E. BERGIN
*Major General, USA*
*The Adjutant General*

J. LAWTON COLLINS
*Chief of Staff, United States Army*


DISTRIBUTION:

*Active Army:*

GSUSA (5); SSUSA (5); Tech Svc (1); Arm & Svc Bd (5); AFF (25); AA Comd (5); OS Maj Comd (5); Base Comd (5); MDW (10); Log Comd (15); A (35); CHQ (10); D (10); B (10); R (10); Bn (10); C (5); FC (25); Sch (250), except 5 (500), USMA (20); PMS & T (2); Gen Dep (1); Dep (except Sec of Gen Dep) (1); GH (1); PE (1), OSD (1); Ars (5); Div Eng (10); Dist 5 (10); T/O & E 5–56 (10); 5–186 (10).

*NG:* D (5); B (3); R (3); Bn (3); C (2); T/O & E 5–56 (5); 5–186 (5).

*ORC:* Same as NG.

For explanation of distribution formula, see SR 310–90–1.

# CONTENTS

*This manual, together with FM 21–30, 28 June 1951, supersedes FM 21–30, 15 October 1943, including C 1, 21 April 1944; C 2, 15 February 1945; and C 3, 28 February 1945*

# CHAPTER 1

## GENERAL

### 1. PURPOSE AND SCOPE

*a.* The purpose of this manual is to describe the topographic symbols and abbreviations authorized for use by all echelons in the interpretation of military maps, overlays, and related activities.

*b.* Some of the symbols appearing on existing maps of older date may not agree entirely with those shown in this manual. Consequently, before any map is used the symbol legend appearing in the margin should be carefully studied.

*c.* The symbols and abbreviations given in this manual are the result of standardization proceedings and are in general agreement with those employed by the British Army, the Canadian Army, the Aeronautical Chart and Information Service of the U. S. Air Force, the Hydrographic Office of the U. S. Navy, the U. S. Coast and Geodetic Survey, the U. S. Forest Service, the U. S. Geological Survey, and the Tennessee Valley Authority.

*d.* Department of the Army units engaged in map making will be guided by AR 300–15, by TM 5–230 insofar as the symbols given as examples do not conflict with those given here, and by the specifications contained in technical publications prepared under the direction of the Chief of Engineers.

*e.* Abbreviations given in this manual are for topographic use only and in some instances conflict with those given in SR 320–50–1, which are authorized for use in military records, publications, correspondence, messages, and in field work. In accordance with SR 320–50–1, abbreviations will not be used if uncertainty may result.

### 2. ORGANIZATION OF MANUAL

This manual is divided into four chapters.

*a.* Chapter 1 gives general information on the use of topographic symbols, gives the basic scales for topographic maps, defines topographic maps, and discusses map detail, map accuracy, and map colors.

*b.* Chapter 2 gives examples and illustrations of topographic symbols arranged by categories, such as drainage features, relief features, and roads.

*c.* Chapter 3 gives topographic abbreviations, their scope and application.

*d.* Chapter 4 discusses marginal information.

### 3. REFERENCES

Appendix I gives a list of publications which give detailed information on maps and mapping, foreign conventional signs and symbols, reference data for the various services, transportation and signal facilities, and abbreviations for administrative and electrically transmitted messages.

### 4. VARIATIONS OF SYMBOLS

Where no symbol is prescribed for a specialized local feature, the map maker is authorized to use a special symbol, providing—

*a.* There is no conflict with symbols shown in this manual.

*b.* Any special symbol used is explained either in the legend of the map or by appropriate labeling within the body of the map so that no uncertainty may result.

### 5. SCALES OF TOPOGRAPHIC MAPS

*a.* Maps fall into the following general scale categories:

| | |
|---|---|
| Small scale _ _ _ _ _ _ _ _ _ _ _ _ _ _ _ _ | 1:600,000 and smaller |
| Medium scale _ _ _ _ _ _ _ _ _ _ _ _ _ | Larger than 1:600,000 but smaller than 1:75,-000 |
| Large scale _ _ _ _ _ _ _ _ _ _ _ _ _ | 1:75,000 and larger |

*b.* Standard scales and nomenclature for Department of the Army Maps are—

Smaller than 1:1,000,000 ..... General map
1:1,000,000 .................. Strategic map
1:250,000 .................... Strategic-tactical map (n o r m a l scale)
1:250,000 .................... Road
1:50,000 ..................... Tactical map (p r e f e r r e d scale)
1:25,000 ..................... Artillery map
1:25,000 ..................... Photomap (preferred scale)
1:12,500 ..................... Town plan

*c.* Depending upon the availability of information and the importance of the area, the following scales are sometimes substituted:

1:500,000 .................... Strategic-tactical map (alternate for 1:250,000)
1:100,000 .................... Tactical map (alternate for 1:50,000)
1:12,500 ..................... Photomap (alternate for 1:25,000)

*d.* All of the above types and scales of maps will not necessarily be available for a particular area. Their issue will be governed by military and logistic considerations.

*e.* Maps with scales different from those given above occasionally will be encountered. Usually, they are foreign military maps. The most common examples are 1:62,500 or 1:63,360 in place of 1:50,000; and 1:253,440 in place of 1:250,000. In the United States, nonmilitary governmental mapping agencies may use other scales such as 1:24,000 or 1:31,680 in place of 1:25,000; and 1:62,500 in place of 1:50,000.

## 6. TOPOGRAPHIC MAPS

*a. General.* A topographic map is a graphic representation to scale, horizontal and vertical, of some portion of the earth's surface, systematically plotted on a plane surface. The ideal situation would be realized if every feature on the portion of the earth being mapped could be shown in its true shape, orientation, and proportion. Unfortunately, such a representation is impossible.

This is evident when one considers that on a map at the scale of 1:50,000, a square mile must be condensed into a small square approximately 1.27 by 1.27 inches. If every feature were plotted true to scale, the resulting map would be impossible to read, for many items would be drawn so minutely as to be unrecognizable even with a magnifying glass. For a map to be intelligible, features must be indicated by symbols. Many of these must necessarily be exaggerated in size for legibility. For example, on a map at the scale of 1:50,000 the prescribed symbol for a small house covers an area corresponding to about 85 feet square, the scaled width of a road measures about 95 feet; the symbol for a single-track railroad occupies a width equivalent to about 165 feet on the ground. Consequently, only the landmarks and important features of an area can be shown. Those shown on a map represent the characteristic pattern of the area and are usually those most readily recognized in the field.

*b. Map Detail.* Map detail represents ground features as they existed at the date of map compilation or latest revision. Since man is continually building, demolishing, and changing ground features, the detail appearing on a map may not exactly match that appearing on the ground. This is especially true in developed areas. The *amount* of detail shown on a map increases with its scale. The map attempts to show the maximum of detail without impairing legibility. In areas of heavy cultural density many of the less important items must be omitted. In areas of sparse density, fewer items are omitted. When deletions are necessary because of the density of detail, care is taken to retain the general pattern of the features in the area. For example, where all buildings of a group cannot be shown, those retained portray the general pattern of the group without exaggerating the area covered. Similarly, where numerous ditches, streams, levees, and the like exist, the less important are omitted and the more important are retained to show the characteristic pattern of the features in the area.

*c. Symbols.* So far as is practicable, a mapped feature is shown by the same symbol on maps of different scales, but certain modifications and departures are necessary because of varying map uses and scales. Normally, symbols resemble the features they represent. The center and the orientation of a symbol usually correspond to the true center and orientation of the feature represented. All line features such as roads, railroads, streams, power lines, and similar features retain, within the limitations of scale, the variations of alignment which actually exist. Along such features as roads the locations of buildings and other features are necessarily displaced because of the exaggerated size of the symbols, and reference to the positions of such features must be made with caution.

*d. Accuracy of Maps.* On a map of 1:1,000,000, a sixteenth of an inch represents approximately 1 mile; on a map of 1:250,000, a quarter of an inch represents approximately 1 mile. It is apparent, then, that on such maps it is impossible to obtain the precise accuracy in plotting possible on large-scale maps. Small- and medium-scale maps normally are compiled from the best available larger-scale maps. Since these sources vary in reliability, the map user should study the coverage diagram shown in the margin of the map to determine the general reliability of the map. On most large-scale maps of areas within the continental limits of the United States, 90 percent of all features shown are within $\frac{1}{50}$ inch of their true geographic positions. The remaining 10 percent are within $\frac{1}{20}$ inch. Ninety percent of the contours are accurate within one-half of the basic contour interval and 90 percent of the spot heights (elevations of particular locations) are accurate within one-fourth of the contour interval. In compiling large-scale maps covering foreign areas, it is not always possible for us to achieve the high standards of accuracy obtainable on maps of the United States. The accuracy standards of such maps usually may be determined from the marginal coverage diagram.

*e. Map Colors.* Topographic symbols usually appear in characteristic colors: black for *cultural* (man-made) features other than roads, blue for *water* features, brown or gray for *relief* features, green for *vegetation*, and red for *road classifications*.

# CHAPTER 2

## TOPOGRAPHIC SYMBOLS

## 7. SCOPE

This chapter illustrates and explains the symbols used on military maps of all scales. The symbols are in general the same for all categories, but because of differences in use and smaller scales, certain symbols are modified or omitted on medium- and small-scale maps.

## 8. DRAINAGE FEATURES

*a.* A *perennial feature* contains water during most of the year.

*b.* An *intermittent feature* contains water during only part of the year. The shore line of an intermittent lake or pond is represented as indefinite and approximate.

*c.* A *dry* or *cyclical feature* or a *wash* is usually dry. The limits of such features are represented as indefinite.

*d.* The following pages contain the approved symbols for Drainage Features.

**Figure 1.  Shore Line.**   The mean high or normal water line is the shore line.
(a)  Definite.   (b)  Indefinite or unsurveyed.

**Figure 2.  Perennial Lake or Pond.**
(a)  Definite shore line.   (b)  Indefinite or unsurveyed shore line.

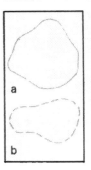  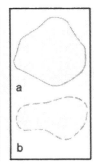 

**Figure 3.  Intermittent Lake or Pond.**

**Figure 4.  Dry or Cyclical Lake or Pond.**

**Figure 5.    Reservoir with Natural Shore Line.**   The shore line is controlled by the height of the dam.

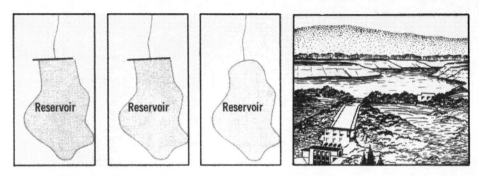

**Figure 6.    Narrow Perennial Stream.**
(a) Surveyed.   (b) Unsurveyed.

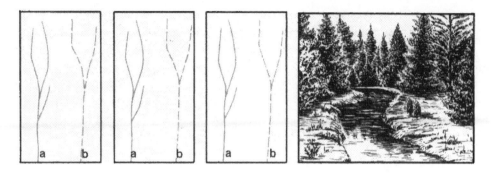

**Figure 7.    Wide Perennial Stream.**
(a) Surveyed.   (b) Unsurveyed.

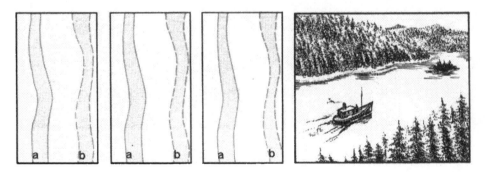

**Figure 8.    Intermittent Stream.**

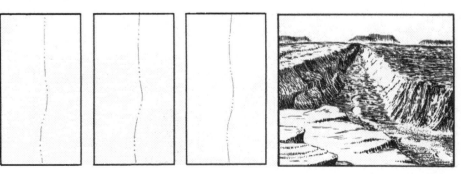

**Figure 9.   Narrow Wash or Dry Stream.**
   (a) United States or foreign.   (b) Foreign (in certain arid areas).

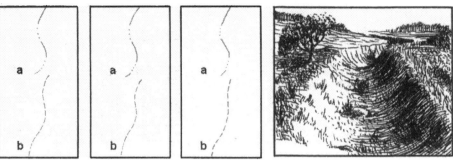

**Figure 10.   Wide Wash or Dry River Bed.**
   (a) United States or foreign.   (b) Foreign (in certain arid areas).

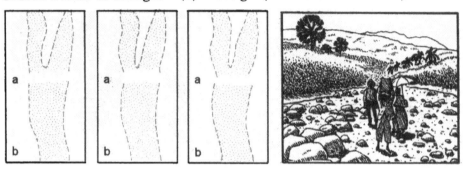

**Figure 11.   Unclassified Stream.**   This symbol is used when a stream cannot be determined to   be either perennial or intermittent.

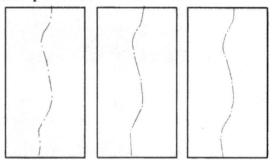

**Figure 12.   Braided Stream.**

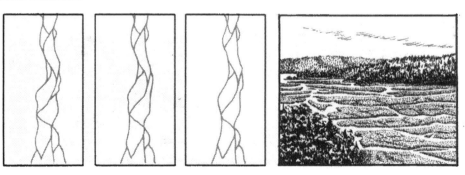

**Figure 13.   Disappearing Stream.**

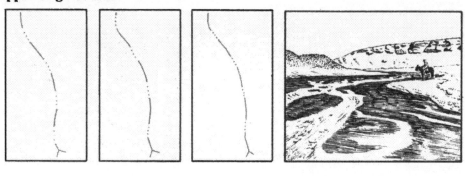

**Figure 14.   Large Rapids.**

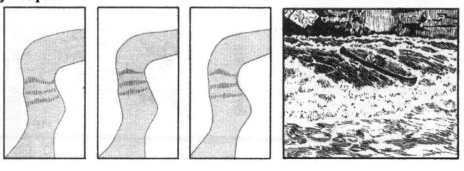

**Figure 15.   Large Falls.**

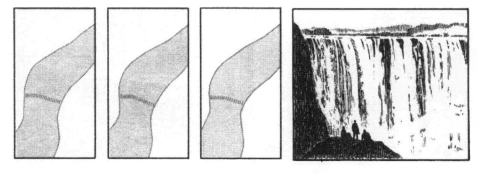

**Figure 16.   Small Rapids.**

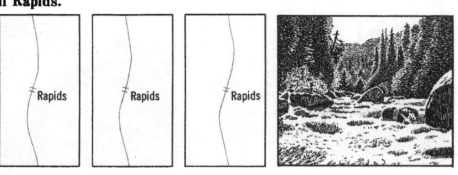

**Figure 17.   Small Falls.**

**Figure 18.   Navigable Canal, in Operation.**
(a) Narrow.   (b) Wide.

**Figure 19.   Abandoned Canal, Containing Water.**
(a) Narrow.   (b) Wide.

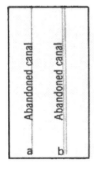   

**Figure 20.   Abandoned Canal, Generally Dry.**
(a) Narrow.   (b) Wide.

**Figure 21.   Perennial Ditch.**

**Figure 22.   Intermittent Ditch.**

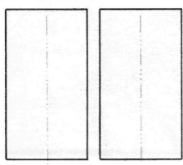 

**Figure 23.   Aqueduct.**   The symbol represents a conduit used for carrying water.   It may be either an open or closed canal.   Water pipelines are symbolized by the aqueduct symbol.

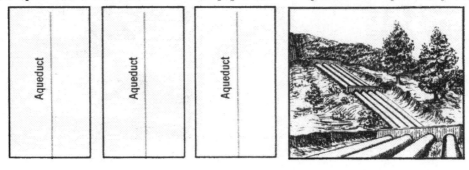

**Figure 24.   Underground Aqueduct, with Outlet.**

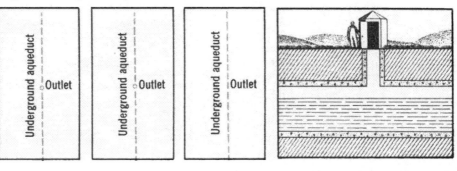

**Figure 25.    Elevated Conduit of Any Type.**

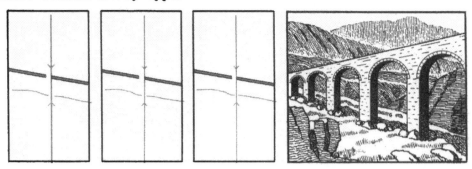

**Figure 26.    Flume, Penstock, and Similar Features.**

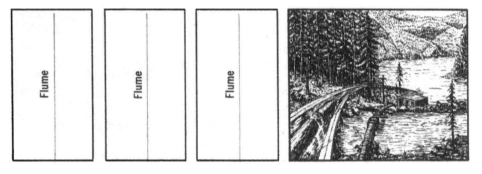

**Figure 27.    Salt Evaporator.**  Only major separations are shown; minor ditches and levees are omitted.

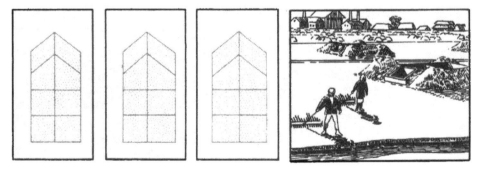

**Figure 28.    Marsh or Swamp.**  No distinction is made between fresh and salt marshes.

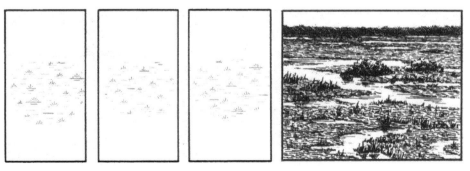

**Figure 29.   Coastal Marsh in Tidal Waters.**   The shore line is drawn as the water side limits of the marsh.

**Figure 30.   Coastal Marsh in Nontidal Waters.**   The shore line is drawn as the true shore line.

**Figure 31.   Hummocks and Ridges in Swamps or Marshes.**

**Figure 32.   Peat Cutting.**   The symbol is representative and does not show the actual shape or the number of cuttings.

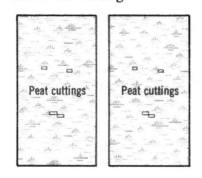

**Figure 33.  Cranberry Bog.**  Only major separations are shown.   The inundation is controlled.

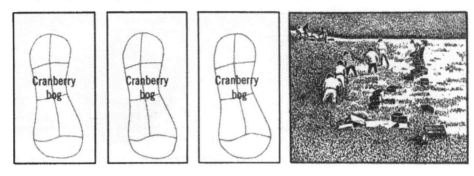

**Figure 34.  Fish Ponds.**   Features of this type are usually shown only on maps of foreign areas.   Only major separations are shown.

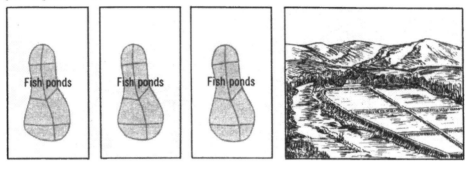

**Figure 35.  Rice Paddy.**  Only fields subject to inundation, either controlled or natural, are shown. Minor ditches and levees are omitted.

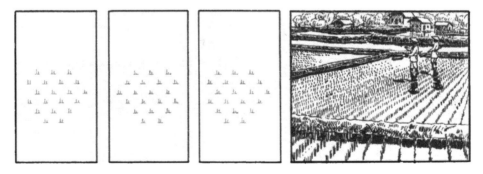

**Figure 36.  Land Subject to Inundation.**  In the United States only those areas subject to controlled inundation are shown.  In foreign areas the inundation may be either controlled or natural.   Areas subject to temporary natural inundation are not symbolized.

**Figure 37.**  **Spring.**  Springs are shown only in arid areas or where they are important landmark features.   If there is enough information, labeling indicates whether the spring is mineral, alkali, undrinkable, hot, and so on.
(a) Perennial.   (b) Intermittent.

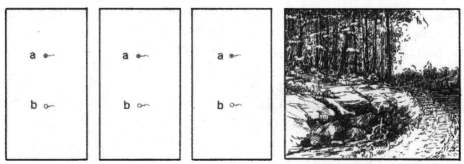

**Figure 38.**  **Well.**  Wells are shown only in arid areas or when they are landmark features.   Walled-in springs, cisterns and underground water tanks are shown as wells.
(a) Perennial.   (b) Intermittent.

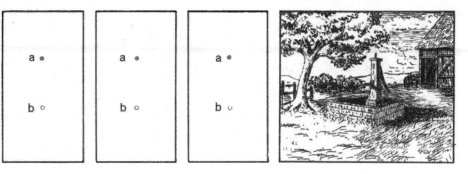

# 9. RELIEF FEATURES

*a. Methods of Showing Relief.* Depending upon the accuracy of information, the shapes of the terrain are shown on a map by lines representing contours, approximate contours, and form lines. Any one or all of these methods may be used on a single map. On medium- and small-scale maps, significant relief features may be shown by hachures when available data are insufficient to warrant the use of contours. On large-scale maps, the lines are usually printed in brown. On medium-scale maps, the lines are usually printed in gray. Also, on medium-scale maps, *hill shading* is usually added over the lines. This creates a three-dimensional effect and permits a ready appreciation of the terrain since the hills and ridges stand out much as they would on a relief map. On small-scale maps the contour lines are usually printed in brown. Normally, on small-scale maps, the contours are supplemented by gradient tints. A key box on each map indicates the elevation bands and their corresponding tints.

*b. Units of Measure.* Except in the United States and a few other countries where the foot is the standard unit of measure, all elevations on military maps are in terms of the meter (39.37 inches or 3.28 feet).

*c. Contours.* Relief is normally shown by contour lines. A contour line on a map represents an imaginary line on the earth's surface, all points of which, within permissible tolerances, are of the same elevation above a fixed datum, usually mean sea level. To aid the map user, every fifth contour is a heavier line. These are commonly referred to as *index* contours. The remaining contours are commonly referred to as *intermediate* contours. In certain areas on a map the normal contour interval is sometimes too large to present significant topographic formations correctly, and *supplementary* half-interval contours are added. On small-scale maps, utilizing gradient tints, index contours are not shown.

*d. Approximate Contours.* Whenever there is any question as to the reliability of the source material or of the survey, *approximate* contours are substituted for normal contours. An approximate contour on a map represents an imaginary line on the earth's surface, all points of which are estimated to be of equal elevation. As with normal contours, a distinction is made between index, intermediate, and supplementary contours.

*e. Contour Intervals.* Contour lines are drawn on a map at definite elevation intervals. Using a given contour interval the lines are far apart in flat areas and close together in hilly areas. Consequently, to present the best picture, the size of the contour interval used varies with the nature of the terrain, although normally a contour interval is constant in a series of map sheets. On sheets where the relief is generally flat or gently rolling, a smaller contour interval is used than on sheets where the relief is generally hilly, and the distance between lines represents smaller differences in elevation. Scale also affects the contour interval; if the contour interval on a 1:25,000 scale map were 5 meters, for example, the interval used on a 1:50,000 map covering the same area would probably be 10 meters.

*f. Form Lines.* When available information is insufficient to warrant the use of either normal or approximate contours, form lines are used. Normally, form lines are used only in areas outside the United States. Form lines collectively portray the general shapes of topographic features, but with little or no reference to a datum plane. They do not present an accurate representation of the terrain, but merely illustrate the general topographic shapes of an area. Since the lines are based on little or no control, their intervals cannot be used to estimate differences in elevations.

*g. Hachures.* Hachures are used on medium- and small-scale maps to indicate promontories where available data are insufficient to warrant the use of normal or approximate contours, but are sufficient to determine the location of the promontories. Hachures are also used in conjunction with normal or approximate contours to indicate important promontories which would not be properly depicted otherwise, because of the contour interval and the nature of the terrain.

*h. Marginal Notes.* Before reading relief from the map, the user should determine the contour interval and the nature of any other methods used to show relief. This information is found in the margin of the map either in the *contour interval note* or the *gradient tint box.* Other special notes pertaining to the relief are sometimes found in the lower margin. The user should also study the *coverage diagram* or *reliability diagram* in the margin to obtain an additional evaluation of contour accuracy.

*i. Symbols.* The following pages contain the approved symbols for Relief Features.

**Figure 39.  Contours.**
    (a) Index.   (b) Intermediate.   (c) Supplementary.

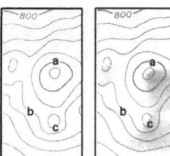  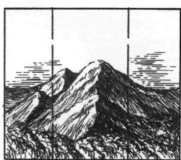

**Figure 40.  Approximate Contours.**
    (a) Index.   (b) Intermediate.   (c) Supplementary.

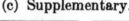     

**Figure 41.  Form Lines.**

**Figure 42.  Hachures.**   This symbol is used to indicate significant formations not revealed by contours.

**17**

**Figure 43.   High Cliff, with Height Equal to or Greater than Contour Interval.**

**Figure 44.   Abrupt Slope or Scarp, With Height Less Than the Contour Interval.**   Features of this type are usually shown only on maps of foreign areas.   The tick marks always point downgrade.

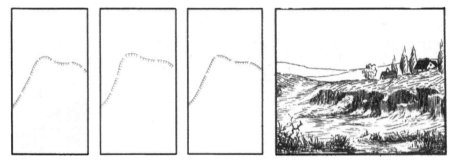

**Figure 45.   Depression, With Depth Less Than Contour Interval.**   The tick marks always point downgrade.

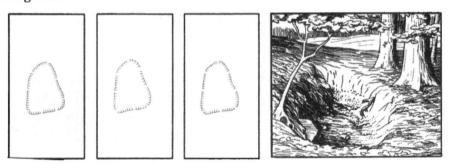

**Figure 46.   Depression, With Depth Greater Than Contour Interval.**   The tick marks always point downgrade.

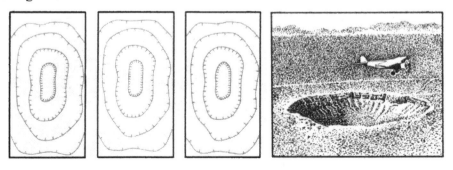

**Figure 47.   Crevice.**   (See also fig. 69, crevasse.)
(a) Large.   (b) Small.

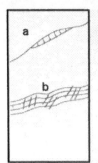 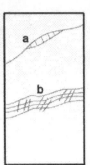 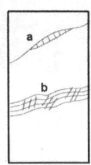 

**Figure 48.   Cut.**   Cuts less in depth than the contour interval are usually omitted.

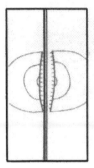 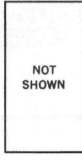  

**Figure 49.   Fill.**   Fills less in height than the contour interval are usually omitted.

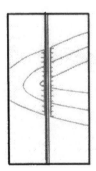 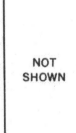 

**Figure 50.   Small Levee.**   Large levees are shown by contours.

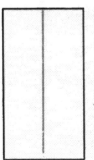 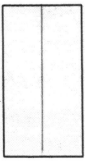 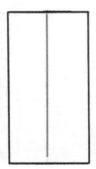 

**Figure 51.  Small Levee Carrying Road.**

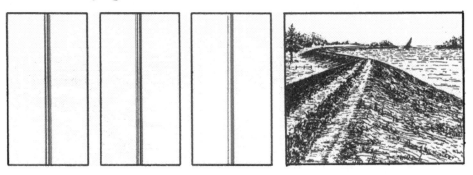

**Figure 52.  Small Levee Carrying Railroad.**

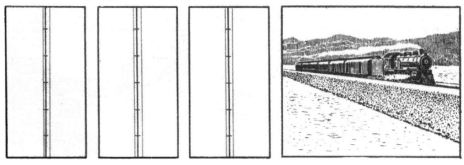

**Figure 53.  Sand.**

**Figure 54.  Sand.**  Alternate of symbol 53; used in certain foreign areas.

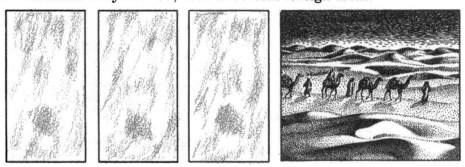

**Figure 55.**   **Crescent Dunes.**   Crescent dunes are shown only on maps of foreign areas.

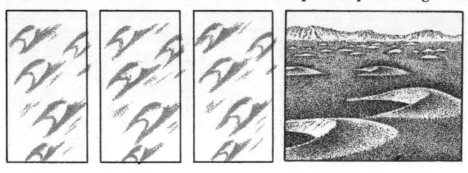

**Figure 56.**   **Lateral Dunes.**   Lateral dunes are shown only on maps of foreign areas.

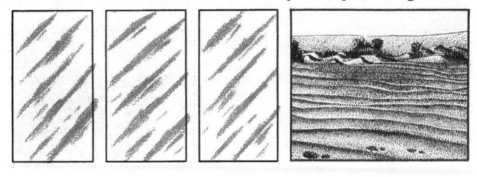

**Figure 57.**   **Wet Sand.**   This symbol is used on maps of foreign areas to show various features whose outstanding characteristic is wet sand.   The map legend defines the symbol.

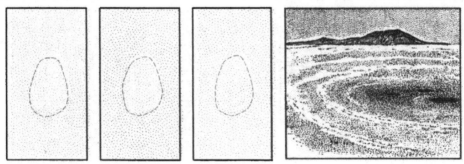

**Figure 58.**   **Sand Beach.**   Sand is defined as aggregate predominantly less than .02 inch in diameter.

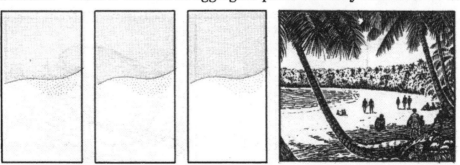

**Figure 59.   Gravel Beach.**   Gravel is defined as aggregate predominantly .2–10 inches in diameter.

**Figure 60.   Boulder-Strewn Beach.**   Boulders are defined as aggregate predominantly over 10 inches in diameter.

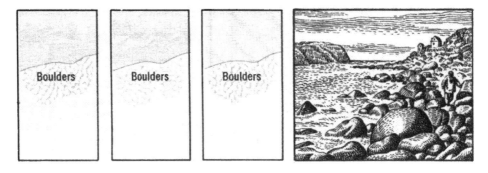

**Figure 61.   Distorted Surface Area.**   The symbol represents such features as gas or oil blisters or bumps found in the midwest United States, rock- or boulder-covered areas, rock outcrops, lava-covered areas, and areas of a similar nature.   Labeling indicates nature.

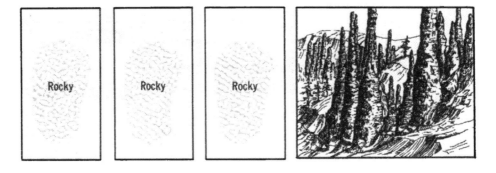

**Figure 62.   Isolated Boulder.**   Isolated boulder is shown only if of enough size or prominence to serve as a landmark.

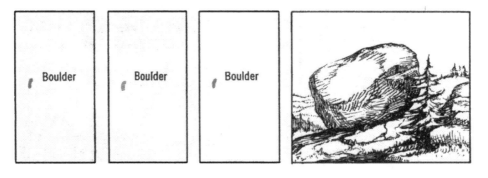

**Figure 63.   Strip Mine, Tailings Pile, Mine Dump.**

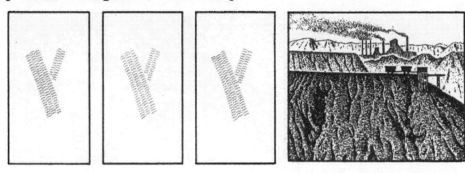

**Figure 64.   Icefield or Snowfield.**   Depending on the available information, formations are shown within the field by either approximate contours (drawn as continuous blue lines) or form lines (drawn as broken blue lines).

**Figure 65.   Glacier.**   Depending on the available information, shapes within the glacial area are shown either by approximate contours (drawn as continuous blue lines) or form lines (drawn as broken blue lines).

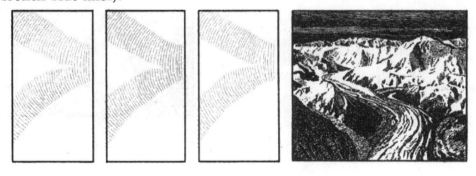

**Figure 66.   Glacial Moraine.**

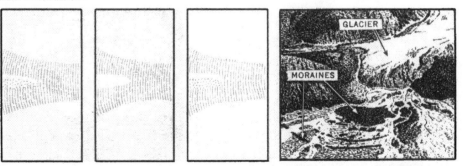

**Figure 67.   High Ice Cliff, With Height Equal to or Greater Than Contour Interval.**

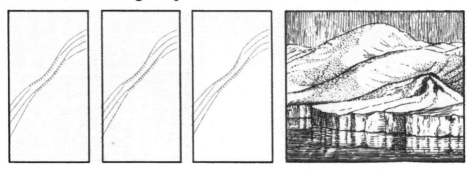

**Figure 68.   Low Ice Cliff, With Height Less Than Contour Interval.** Only those of landmark nature are shown.   Ticks always point downgrade.

**Figure 69.   Crevasse.** (See also fig. 47, crevice.)   Crevasses are constantly forming and disappearing; the symbols indicate areas in which crevasses exist.
(a) Large.   (b) Small.

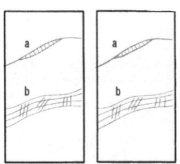

**Figure 70.   Cave.** Only important caves and those of a landmark nature are shown.   The "V" marks the location of the entrance and the shaft marks the general direction of the cave.
(a) Land cave.   (b) Ice cave.

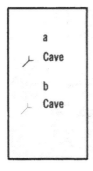
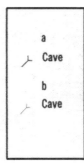
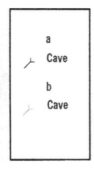
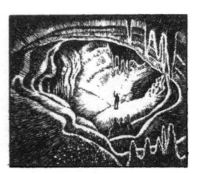

**Figure 71.  Asphalt Lake.**

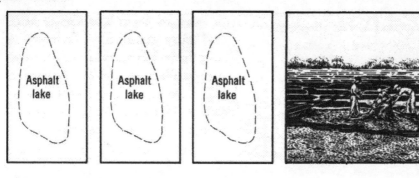

**Figure 72.  Mountain Pass.**

# 10. VEGETATION FEATURES

*a. General.* Although special care is taken in mapping woodland cover, vegetation in many areas is subject to rapid growth or to elimination by cutting or burning. Before using the map, the user should determine the last date of information of the map (found in the notes in the lower left margin) and gage the reliability of the woodland information accordingly. The symbols used indicate such features as cover suitable for the concealment of troops, obstacles to free passage, and landmarks in areas bearing little vegetation. On small-scale maps, particularly the 1 : 1,000,000 scale, the vegetation is usually omitted entirely.

*b. Growths Shown.* Only perennial types of growth are mapped. Isolated trees and low scattered growths are usually omitted. Small clumps of growths are usually omitted, except where they serve as landmarks in areas of little woodland cover. Small clearings are also usually omitted. In certain areas the limits and types of growth are fairly constant. In such cases a distinction may have been made on the map between deciduous, coniferous, and brushwood growths. In many other cases, lack of information or the changing nature and limits of growths makes it impractical to make such a distinction.

*c. Continuous Cover.* The presence of a vegetation symbol does not necessarily mean that the area is completely covered. Depending upon the area, growth having as little as 20 to 35 percent canopy cover is symbolized as continuous.

*d. Symbols.* The following pages contain the approved symbols for vegetation features.

**Figure 73.    Woods or Brushwood (when No Distinction is Made).** Any perennial vegetation of enough stand or height to conceal troops, or which is thick enough to be a serious obstacle to free passage is classified as woods or brushwood.  No distinction is made between woods and brushwood or between different types of vegetation.  (a) and (b) are alternate symbols.

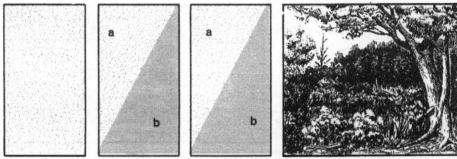

**Figure 74.    Coniferous Woods (when a Distinction is Made).**  No distinction is made on medium- and small-scale maps.    (a) and (b) are alternate symbols.

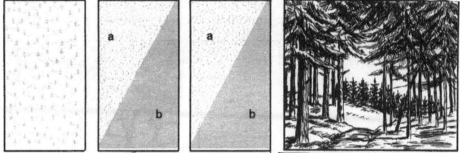

**Figure 75.    Deciduous Woods (when a Distinction is Made).**  No distinction is made on medium- and small-scale maps.    (a) and (b) are alternate symbols.

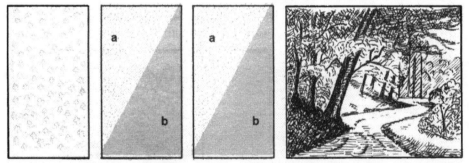

**Figure 76.    Mixed Woods (when a Distinction is Made).**  No distinction is made on medium- and small-scale maps.    (a) and (b) are alternate symbols.

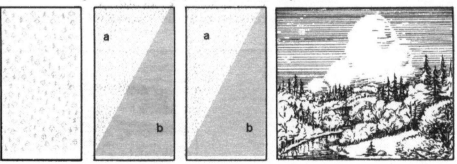

**27**

**Figure 77.   Scrub.**  Scrub growth includes cactus, stunted shrubs, sagebrush, mesquite, and similar plants of low growth which present an obstacle to free passage or which serve as land-marks in desert areas.

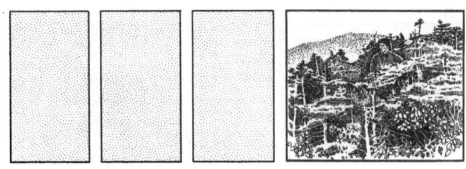

**Figure 78.   Orchard or Plantation.**  An area of orchards or plantations usually consists of rows of evenly spaced trees, showing evidence of planned planting.   The type of growth is indi-cated except when it is of the common fruit variety, such as apple, orange, pear, or the like.

**Figure 79.   Vineyard.**  Vine growths which are not perennial are omitted.   No indication as to the type of growth is given.

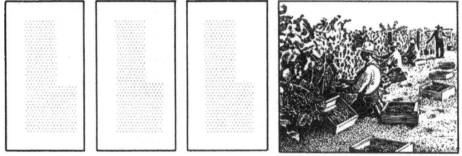

**Figure 80.   Tropical Grass.**  The symbol represents a dense growth of tall grass found in tropical or semitropical regions.

**Figure 81.    Mangrove.**   Mangrove is an impenetrable growth existing in tidal waters of tropical and semitropical areas.   The shore line shown on the seaside indicates the outer limits of mangrove and does not represent the mean high water line.   Channels through mangrove are shown.

**Figure 82.    Nipa.**   Nipa is a stemless palm growing in tidal or brackish waters in tropical climates adjacent to coast lines.   The shore line as shown is the outer limits and is not the mean high water line.

**Figure 83.    Marshy Areas in Northern Latitudes.**   This symbol represents features such as tundra in the USSR, muskeg in Canada, etc.   The nature of the feature is indicated by labeling.

# 11. COASTAL HYDROGRAPHY

a. *General.* Coastal hydrographic features and notes pertinent to those features are usually shown on all sheets showing navigable waters. Sheets showing land areas bordering on inland bodies of water, such as lakes, contain only offshore data. Sheets showing land areas bordering on oceans, seas, bays, or similar bodies of water contain both offshore and foreshore data.

b. *Definition of Coastal Terms* (fig. 84).

(1) *Coastal hydrographic features.* All features within the foreshore and offshore areas including permanent cultural and natural features which affect the navigability of the area.

(2) *Foreshore area.* That area which is bare or awash at the hydrographic datum (low water) but which is covered at mean high water.

(3) *Offshore area.* That area which is covered at the hydrographic datum.

(4) *Hydrographic datum.* That stage of low tide to which depths are referred. This varies somewhat in different parts of the world.

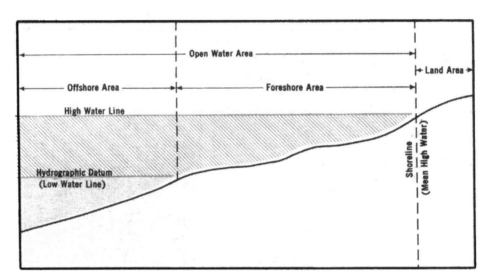

Figure 84. Definition of Coastal Terms.

c. *Symbols.* The following pages contain the approved symbols for coastal hydrographic features.

**Figure 85.    Foreshore Flat.**   A foreshore flat occurs only in tidal waters.   It is generally devoid of vegetation and is composed of sand, gravel, boulders, mud, clay, or any combination of such materials.   Labeling indicates the type of composition.   Labeling is omitted if the feature is small or its composition indefinable.

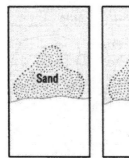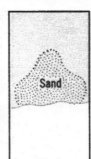

**Figure 86.    Reef or Ledge.**   Labeling indicates whether the reef is of rock or coral.
(a) Large.    (b) Small.

**Figure 87.    Sunken Rock.**   Rock covered at all stages of the tide.   Only rocks which are actual dangers to navigation are shown on medium- and small-scale maps.
(a) Potential danger to navigation.    (b) Actual danger to navigation.

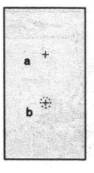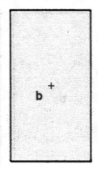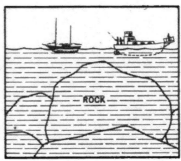

**Figure 88.   Rock, Bare, or Awash.**  This symbol represents rocks exposed or awash at the hydrographic datum.  Only rocks which are actual dangers to navigation are shown on medium- and small-scale maps.

(a) Potential danger to navigation.   (b) Actual danger to navigation.

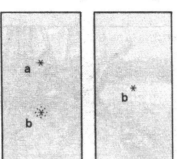 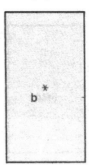 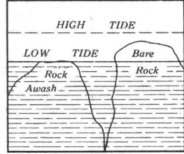

**Figure 89.   Exposed Wreck.**  A wreck is exposed when any portion of its hull is above water at the hydrographic datum plane.  The circle of the symbol marks the location of the wreck.

**Figure 90.   Sunken Wreck.**  The symbol represents wrecks which are less than 10 fathoms (60 feet) deep, with no part of the hull above water at the hydrographic datum.  Masts may or may not be above water.  The center of the symbol marks the location of the wreck.  Only actual dangers are shown on medium- and small-scale maps.

(a) Potential danger to navigation.   (b) Actual danger to navigation.

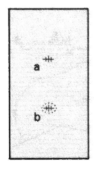  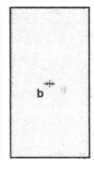 

**Figure 91.**  **Sunken Danger or Obstruction.**  Labeling indicates the nature of the feature. (a) Least depth indicated.  (b) Depth determined by wire drag.

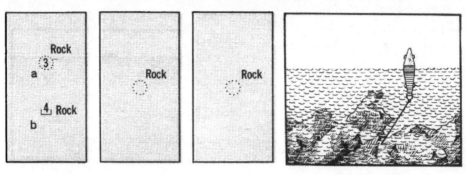

**Figure 92.**  **Limit of Danger Line.**  A danger line outlines any feature which is a danger to navigation, such as rocks, foul ground, shoals, small reefs and similar obstructions.  Labeling usually is added to indicate the nature of the danger.

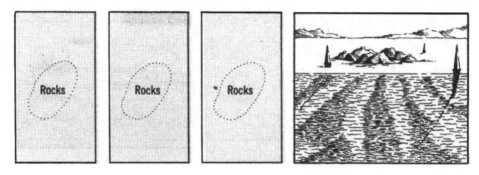

**Figure 93.**  **Sounding.**  The depth of the bottom at hydrographic datum is usually expressed in fathoms (6 feet).  Depths are given in feet in the eastern United States and on the Gulf Coast. The map legend indicates the unit of measure.

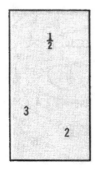 

**Figure 94.   No-Bottom Sounding.**   The symbol represents soundings for which true depths have not been determined.   The value indicates the depth sounded without bottom being struck.

    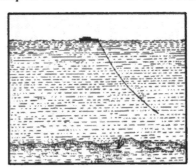

**Figure 95.   Swept Depth.**   The figure in the bracket indicates the depth of clearance.   This is not necessarily the actual depth.   Labeling describes the nature of any danger.

**Figure 96.   Depth Curves.**   A depth curve is a line drawn on a map to represent an imaginary line on the sea bottom, all points of which are at an equal depth below the hydrographic datum.   Values labeling depth curves are in the same unit of measure as the soundings.

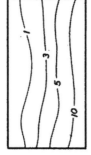  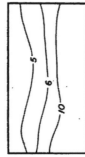  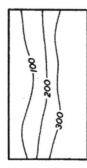  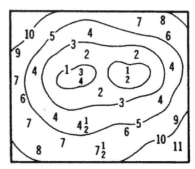

**Figure 97.** **Bottom Characteristics.** The character or composition of the bottom is indicated by labeling.

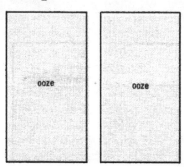 

**Figure 98.** **Breaker.**
(a) Limits known. (b) Limits unknown.

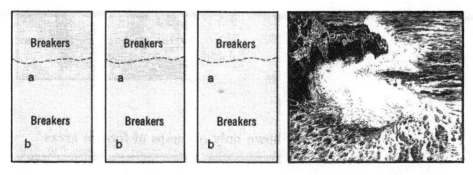

**Figure 99.** **Current.** If the speed is known, it is indicated in knots.
(a) General. (b) Flood. (c) Ebb.

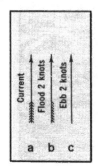 

**Figure 100.　Area Limits.**　The symbol represents the limits of anchorages, fishing stakes, fishing weirs, cable areas, dredged channels, dredge dumps, pipeline areas, prohibited areas, spoil ground, swept areas, and similar areas.

 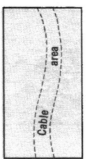 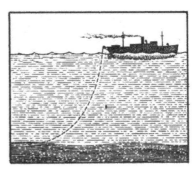

**Figure 101.　Dolphin, Piling, Stump, Snag.**　Appropriate labeling indicates the type of obstruction.

**Figure 102.　Anchorage for Large Vessels.**　Shown only on maps of foreign areas.

**Figure 103.　Anchorage for Small Vessels.**　Shown only on maps of foreign areas.

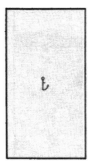  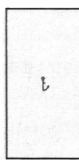 

# 12. ROADS IN THE UNITED STATES ON LARGE- AND MEDIUM-SCALE MAPS

*a. Road Classifications on Large-Scale Maps.* Roads within the continental limits of the United States are classified on large-scale maps as—

    (1) Hard-surface, heavy-duty roads:
        (*a*) Four or more lanes wide.
        (*b*) Two or three lanes wide.
    (2) Hard-surface, medium-duty roads:
        (*a*) Four or more lanes wide.
        (*b*) Two or three lanes wide.
    (3) Improved light-duty roads.
    (4) Unimproved dirt roads.
    (5) Trails.

*b. Road Classifications on Medium-Scale Maps.* The classifications on medium-scale maps are the same, except for hard-surface roads, where a distinction is made between roads two lanes wide and roads more than two lanes wide.

*c. Hard-Surface, Heavy-Duty Roads.* Roads of this classification carry heavy truck loads in all weather with a minimum of maintenance. The construction is usually of portland-cement concrete, bituminous concrete, or sheet asphalt, rock asphalt, bituminous penetration, or mixed bituminous on a heavy foundation. Brick or block roads are also included in this category.

*d. Hard-Surface, Medium-Duty Roads.* These roads carry medium-heavy truck loads in all weather. Occasional maintenance is required. Construction is usually a bituminous-penetration or mixed-bituminous surface, or bituminous-treated surface on a light foundation.

*e. Improved, Light-Duty Roads.* These roads carry light loads in all weather. Periodical maintenance is usually necessary. Construction consists of stabilized or oiled-surface gravel or stone, graded and drained gravel or stone, or graded and drained soil surface. Included in this category are hard-surfaced roads less than two lanes wide and improved private roads which normally are not practical for use in rerouting of traffic in emergencies.

*f. Unimproved Dirt Roads.* These roads are suitable only for light loads in dry weather. They are without surface improvement and are seldom maintained. Included are abandoned roads, fire roads, and lumber roads.

*g. Trails.* The map shows important foot paths, foot trails, and pack trails which can accommodate ¼-ton trucks in dry weather. Minor and short connecting trails are usually omitted.

*h. Symbols.* The following pages contain the approved symbols for Roads in the United States.

**Figure 104.   Hard-Surface, Heavy-Duty Road.**
LARGE-SCALE:  Four or more lanes wide.
MEDIUM-SCALE:  Three or more lanes wide.
Labeling indicates the number of lanes.

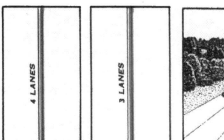 

**Figure 105.   Hard-Surface, Heavy-Duty Road.**
LARGE-SCALE:  Two or three lanes wide.    Unless otherwise labeled, the road is two lanes wide.
MEDIUM-SCALE:  Two lanes wide.

**Figure 106.   Hard-Surface, Medium-Duty Road.**
LARGE-SCALE:  Four or more lanes wide.
MEDIUM-SCALE:  Three or more lanes wide.
Labeling indicates the number of lanes.

**Figure 107.   Hard-Surface, Medium-Duty Road.**
LARGE SCALE:  Two or three lanes wide.   Unless otherwise labeled, the road is two lanes wide.
MEDIUM-SCALE:  Two lanes wide.

**Figure 108.   Improved, Light-Duty Road.**

**Figure 109.   Unimproved Dirt-Road.**

**Figure 110.   Trail.**

## 13. ROADS IN FOREIGN AREAS ON LARGE- AND MEDIUM-SCALE MAPS

*a. Road Classifications.* Roads outside the continental limits of the United States are classified on both large- and medium-scale maps as—

(1) Hard-surface, all weather-roads:
   (a) more than two lanes wide.
   (b) two lanes wide.
   (c) less than two lanes wide.
(2) Loose-surface, graded, all-weather roads.
(3) Loose-surface, dry-weather, or dirt-roads.
(4) Tracks.
(5) Trails.

*b. Hard-Surface, All-Weather Road.* These roads carry fairly heavy truck loads in all weather. Minimum maintenance requirements are periodical inspection and repair. The construction is usually concrete or asphaltic concrete, bituminous macadam, surface treated oiled gravel, or light tarbound macadam.

*c. Loose-Surface, Graded, All-Weather Road.* These carry light loads in all-weather. The roads are generally drained and graded. Periodical maintenance is required. Construction is usually of gravel, stone, or some stable material, such as sand-clay, on a light foundation.

*d. Loose-Surface, Dry-Weather or Dirt-Road.* These roads carry light loads in dry weather only. The road may or may not be graded or drained and requires continual maintenance. Any surfacing consists of gravel, or sand-clay with a poor foundation.

*e. Track.* Tracks include winter roads, caravan routes, and natural roadways, and can accommodate very light vehicles, such as ¼-ton trucks, in dry weather. Tracks are normally shown only in areas having poor road systems.

*f. Trails.* Trails include important foot trails, foot paths, and pack trails. Minor trails and unimportant connecting trails are omitted. In areas with good road systems, tracks are included in this category.

*g. Symbols.* The following pages contain the approved symbols for Roads in Foreign Areas.

**Figure 111.   Hard-Surface, All-Weather Road, More Than Two Lanes Wide.**   Labeling indicates the number of lanes.

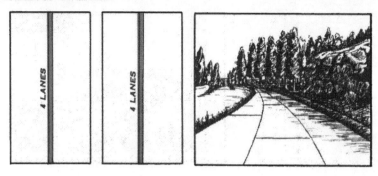

**Figure 112.   Hard-Surface, All-Weather Road, Two Lanes Wide.**

**Figure 113.   Hard-Surface, All-Weather Road, Less Than Two Lanes Wide.**

**Figure 114.   Loose-Surface, Graded, All-Weather Road.**   Medium-scale:
(a) Principal.   (b) Other.

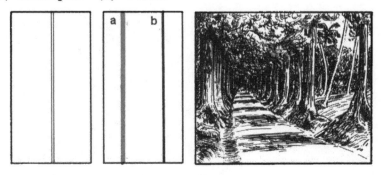

**Figure 115.   Loose-Surface, Dry-Weather, or Dirt-Road.**   Medium-scale:
(a) Principal.   (b) Other.

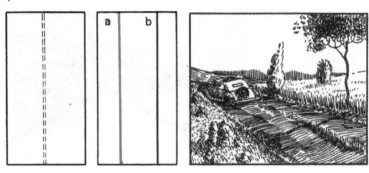

**Figure 116.   Track.**

**Figure 117.   Trail.**

# 14. ROADS ON SMALL-SCALE MAPS

*a. Road Classifications.* Roads on all small-scale maps are classified as—

(1) Dual or super highways.
(2) Main roads.
(3) Secondary roads.
(4) Other roads.
(5) Tracks or trails.

*b. Main Roads.* Main roads are those roads which serve as the main thoroughfares between the important populated places of an area. Well aligned roads of a substantial width and surface which connect a number of populated places, and cross-country roads which form a direct route connecting with roads and trails leading to important features are included in this category. Main roads are generally hard surfaced except in areas with poor road systems.

*c. Secondary Roads.* Secondary roads include those roads connecting the minor cities and towns of an area. A road connecting two main roads, at least one of which is higher in classification than the connecting road, is included in this category. In comparison with main roads, secondary roads have less reported use and less substantial construction, and are generally loose-surfaced roads.

*d. Other Roads.* Included in this category are local-community roads serving the villages and settlements of an area. Also included are those connecting roads important to the communications network but obviously of a lower classification than the secondary roads. Such roads may be loose-surfaced or dirt roads.

*e. Tracks or Trails.* Tracks and trails are symbolized alike. Both are normally shown only in areas of sparse culture where they supply the only means of communication. Minor tracks and trails are omitted. Included in this category are winter roads and caravan routes. Normally, the roadway is natural with little or no improvements.

*f. Symbols.* The following pages contain the approved symbols for roads on small-scale maps.

**Figure 118.   Dual or Super Highway.**

**Figure 119.   Main Road.**

**Figure 120.   Secondary Road.**

**Figure 121.   Other Road.**

**Figure 122.   Track or Trail.**

# 15. ROADS, GENERAL

The following symbols indicate features allied with roads.

| Large Scale | Medium Scale | Small Scale | Illustration |
|---|---|---|---|

**Figure 123.** **Dual Highway.** A dual highway consists of two or more lanes on each side of a physical separation such as a parkway. Surface and construction are indicated by the proper red fill. The number of lanes is indicated by labeling. When scale permits, each side of the highway is symbolized separately.

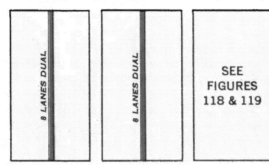

**Figure 124.** **Road Under Construction.** Only roads on which construction is actually under way are shown. If information is available, the classification of the completed road is shown by the proper red fill. Proposed roads are omitted.

**Figure 125.** **Point of Change in Number of Lanes of Extra-Width Road.**

**Figure 126.   Route Marker.**     (a) Federal or national.     (b) State, province or equivalent.

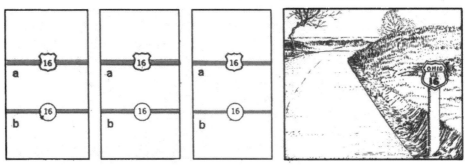

**Figure 127.   Streets in Developed Areas.**   In areas having a developed street pattern, streets are shown to agree with the cultural density and the scale of the map.   Normally, streets are symbolized alike regardless of construction.   If width permits, a street is shown to scale.   Alleys are not shown.   Through routes are indicated by red fills.

**Figure 128.   Street Ending at Barrier or Embankment.**

**Figure 129.   Traffic Circle.**   These are sometimes omitted on 1:50,000 scale maps, especially in congested areas.

**Figure 130.   Cloverleaf.**   A cloverleaf is shown to true shape wherever the scale permits.   They are sometimes omitted on 1:50,000 scale maps, especially in congested areas.

**Figure 131.   Steep Gradients on Roads.**

**Figure 132.   Road Distances.**   This symbol is shown only in foreign areas.   Distances are shown between towns and road junctions.

# 16. RAILROADS

*a. Gage.*

(1) Normal gage is the gage used on the majority of the main line railroads of a country. Normal gage in the continental United States is standard (4' 8½'') gage.

(2) Broad gage is any gage greater than the normal gage used in a country.

(3) Narrow gage is any gage lesser than the normal gage used in a country.

(4) Either the symbol legend in the margin or labeling on the map identifies the gage of the railroads.

*b. Multiple-Track.* A multiple-track railroad contains three or more mainline tracks paralleling each other. The number of tracks of a multiple-track railroad is indicated by labeling placed parallel to the symbol.

*c. Nonoperating Railroad.* A nonoperating railroad is one not in use. Included in this category are railroads under construction, abandoned railroads, and destroyed railroads. Labeling placed parallel to the symbol indicates whether the line is abandoned, destroyed, or under construction.

(1) An abandoned or destroyed railroad is one which is no longer in use but the ballast, bridges, and tracks of which remain in major part and could be put into limited or full operation with a minimum of repair.

(2) Only those railroads on which actual work is under way are symbolized as under construction. Proposed lines are not shown. An operating line sometimes has additional tracks under construction. The symbol for the operating line is shown with appropriate labeling to indicate the construction.

*d. Dismantled Railroads, or Proposed Railroads.* Where the grade has been left intact or actually completed and can be used for any purpose the route will be shown and appropriately labeled.

*e. Electrified.* Electrified railroads are shown by the proper symbol indicating the gage and number of tracks, with the word *Electrified* added parallel to the symbol.

*f. Developed areas.*

(1) Minor lines and sidings are sometimes omitted in congested areas. Through lines are always shown.

(2) Railroads which run underground for long distances in a city are not shown. The dashed lines indicating tunnels are omitted. Only the headwalls and wings of the tunnel entrances are shown.

(3) Subways are not shown.

*g. Symbols.* The following pages contain the approved symbols for Railroads and Related Features.

**Figure 133.** **Single-Track Railroad, in Operation.**
    (a) Normal or broad gage. (b) Narrow gage. Broad and narrow gage railroads are labeled as to gage.

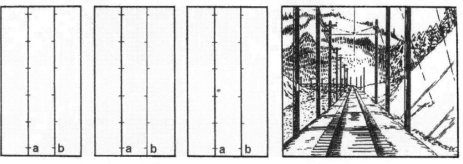

**Figure 134.** **Single-Track Railroad, Nonoperating.** Labeling indicates whether railroad is abandoned, destroyed, or under construction.
    (a) Normal or broad gage. (b) Narrow gage. Broad and narrow gage railroads are labeled as to gage.

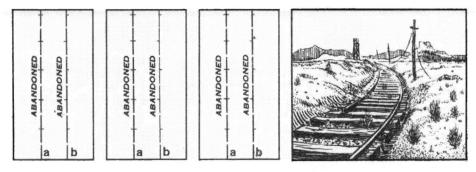

**Figure 135.** **Double- or Multiple-Track Railroad, in Operation.** Railroad is double-track if not otherwise labeled.
    (a) Normal or broad gage. (b) Narrow gage. (c) Standard gage (for use in United States only). Broad gage railroads are labeled as to gage.

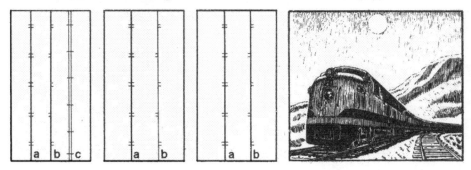

**Figure 136.  Double- or Multiple-Track Railroad, Nonoperating.**  Labeling indicates whether railroad is abandoned, destroyed, or under construction. (a) Normal or broad gage. (b) Narrow gage. (c) Standard gage (for use in United States only). Broad gage railroads are labeled as to gage.

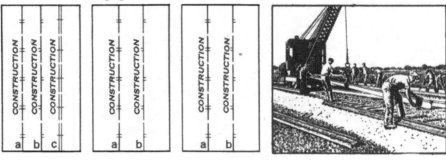

**Figure 137.  Point of Change in the Gage or the Number of Tracks.**

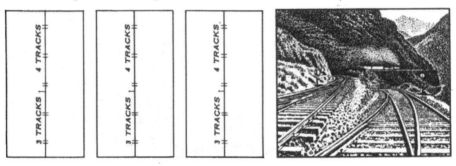

**Figure 138.  Railroad in Street or Wharf.**  Normal symbols are used if the width of the containing feature permits.

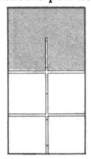

**Figure 139.   Railroad Siding.**   Included are tracks for passing, storage, and loading and unloading of passengers or freight.   In congested areas, sidings are sometimes omitted.

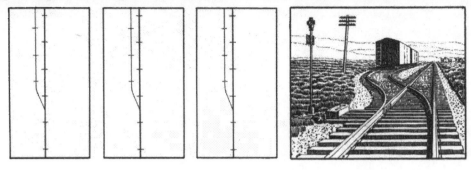

**Figure 140.   Railroad Yard.**   The limiting sidings indicate the correct shape of the yard.   Lines inside the outline are symbolic and do not show the correct number of sidings.

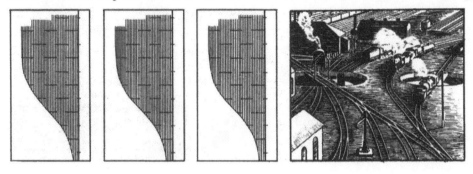

**Figure 141.   Railroads in Juxtaposition.**   Railroads of different ownership closely parallel to each other.

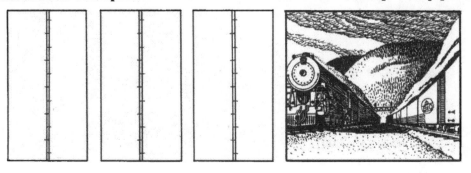

**Figure 142.**  **Turntable.**  A turntable is not drawn to scale.  It is usually omitted in congested areas.

**Figure 143.**  **Railroad Station.**  Within built-up areas, stations are shown only when they are significant as landmarks.  If the building is identifiable, it appears in correct location.  Halts and flag stops having no permanent buildings are indicated by labeling only.

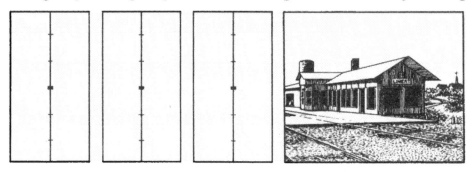

**Figure 144.**  **Railroad Snow Shed.**

**Figure 145.   Car Line.**   Car lines are shown only in open areas; they are omitted in developed areas, streets, and roads.   If the line is not in operation, labeling indicates whether it is abandoned, destroyed, or under construction.   Single- and double-track lines are shown by the same symbol.

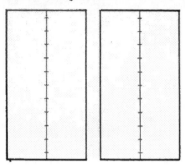 

**Figure 146.   Aerial Cableway.**

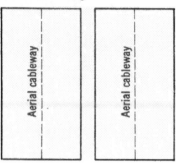 

**Figure 147.   Ski Lift.**

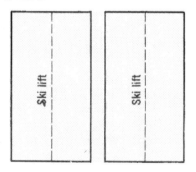 

**Figure 148.   Conveyor Belt.**

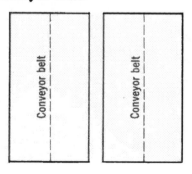 

**Figure 149.  Dismantled Railroad or Car Line.**  Used when the major parts of the tracks and bridges
have been removed.

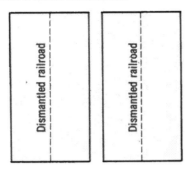

## 17. FEATURES RELATED TO COMMUNICATIONS

a. *Overpasses and Underpasses.* On large-scale maps overpasses and underpasses are normally shown wherever they exist. On medium- and small-scale maps they are generally shown only in open areas. An overpass is a short viaduct carrying a road or railroad above the grade of another road or railroad. An underpass is a short tunnel carrying a road or railroad below the grade of another road or railroad.

b. *Bridges and Viaducts.*

(1) The distinction between a bridge and viaduct is that a bridge passes over what is predominantly water while a viaduct passes over what is predominantly land.

(2) Long bridges or viaducts are always shown. A shorter bridge or viaduct is shown if it serves as an identifiable landmark or is the only means of crossing within the general area.

(3) On long bridges or viaducts the ends of the symbol appear in their correct locations. On shorter ones the symbol is merely representative and the ends are not necessarily in their correct locations.

(4) Bridges and viaducts less than 20 feet long are normally not shown. Culverts are never shown.

(5) When a bridge is used to carry both a road and a railroad on either the same or different levels, the feature is shown by the road-bridge symbol with the railroad shown to the bridge ends. The symbol is labeled "Road and railroad".

c. *Drawbridges.*

(1) Drawbridges are structures of which either the whole or part can be raised, lowered, pivoted, or turned aside to allow or to interrupt traffic.

(2) On large-scale maps the small circle of the symbol is centered on the true location of the center of the movable part of the bridge.

d. *Ferries.*

(1) Ferries capable of carrying vehicular or railroad traffic are normally shown wherever they exist.

(2) Ferries for pedestrians are shown only in areas of sparse culture or when they provide the only means of water-crossing in the general area.

(3) The dashed line connects the points between which the ferry operates, without regard for the actual navigating course of the ferry.

(4) Steamship lines are not shown.

e. *Fords.* Fords are shown only in areas of sparse culture or where they provide the only means of water-crossing in the general area.

f. *Symbols.* The following pages contain the approved symbols for Features Related to Communications.

**Figure 150. Overpass or Underpass.** (a) Two-level crossing. (b) Three-level crossing.

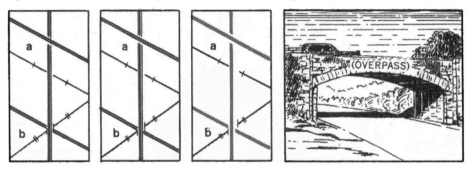

**Figure 151. Grade Crossing.** This symbol is employed only when this feature requires special emphasis.

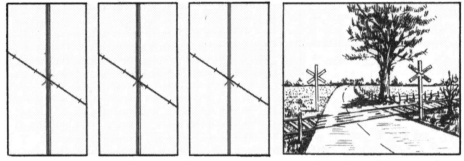

**Figure 152. Road Tunnel.** Road classification fills are omitted within the tunnel.

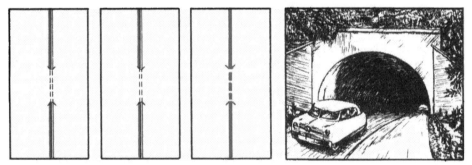

**Figure 153. Railroad Tunnel.** The railroad symbol is omitted within the tunnel.

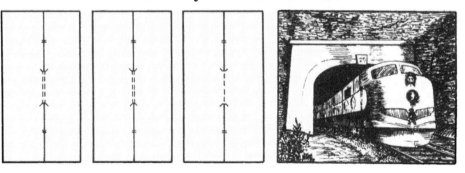

**Figure 154.　Railroad Bridge or Viaduct.**

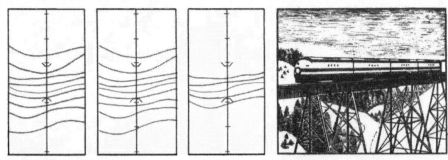

**Figure 155.　Railroad Drawbridge.**

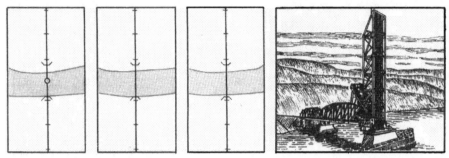

**Figure 156.　Highway Bridge or Viaduct.**

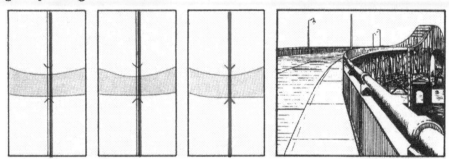

**Figure 157.　Highway Drawbridge.**

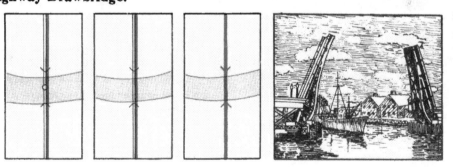

**Figure 158.   Footbridge.**

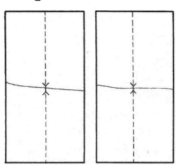 

**Figure 159.   Ferry.**

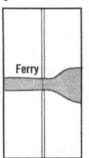 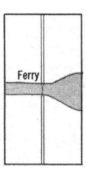  

**Figure 160.   Ford.**

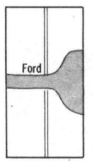 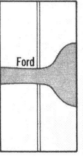  

# 18. BUILDINGS AND POPULATED PLACES ON LARGE-SCALE MAPS

a. *Built-Up Areas.*

(1) A built-up area is a large continuous area which is developed or is in the advanced stage of development for occupancy by concentrated populations. It is usually laid out in a definite street pattern and normally contains a business or industrial district. Since all buildings cannot be shown individually, the area is indicated by an over-all screened red tint.

(2) Only landmark buildings are shown individually in built-up areas. These are buildings which are prominent because of size, location, or usage such as government or public buildings, colleges, schools, churches, hospitals, railroad stations, markets, factories, and buildings of historical or cultural interest.

(3) Within the general outline of the built-up area, individual symbols are used and the built-up area-tint is generally omitted for the following features:

(a) Parks and cemeteries equivalent to or larger than one block.

(b) Institutions such as colleges, schools, and hospitals possessing open ground areas equivalent to or larger than one block.

(c) Sections with little construction or development if equivalent to or larger than two blocks.

(4) All woodland cover is omitted in built-up areas.

b. *Native Settlements.* These include native settlements in foreign areas in which the buildings are not usually of permanent construction. Kampongs in southwestern Asia and encampments in western Africa are examples. The symbol legend of the map defines the symbol properly.

c. *Buildings in General.*

(1) Conventional symbols are used to show a small building or a small structure similar to a building. The symbol is shown in correct orientation and its center usually coincides with the correct location of the center of the structure.

(2) Buildings and similar structures whose plotted size exceeds the conventional symbols are shown in correct orientation and shape and usually in correct location.

(3) Buildings and structures located along roads are shown in their correct location unless they would then fall within the road. In such cases, the symbol is moved back.

(4) In many cases it is impossible to show all buildings because of congestion. The map retains the general shape and pattern of the areas and omits the less important buildings.

d. *Structures Similar to Buildings.*

(1) These are features of substantial construction not definable as buildings. In many instances they are roofed although not necessarily enclosed on all sides. The term includes barns, grandstands, railroad sheds, large open sheds, fruit packing sheds, snow sheds, open-air refineries, and similar structures.

(2) Structures which are smaller than the average dwelling in the locality are not shown.

(3) In foreign areas, when information is unavailable, no distinction is made between buildings and structures similar to buildings.

e. *Schools and Churches.*

(1) When a building is used both as a church and a school, it is symbolized as a school.

(2) In the United States the church symbol is used commonly for all denominations. On maps of foreign areas, this symbol usually denotes a Christian place of worship, with other symbols being used to denote places of worship of other sects. In such cases, the marginal symbol legend should be consulted for detailed information.

(3) When a school has numerous buildings, the flag symbol is shown only on the administration building or the most prominent building in the group.

(4) When there are numerous religious buildings in a group, as in a convent or monastery, the cross symbol is shown only on the building used for religious services or the most prominent building in the group.

*f. Ruins.* Ruins are buildings or structures in such a state of dilapidation or decay that they can no longer be used for their original purpose. Ruins which are smaller than the average dwelling in the locality are not shown unless they possess unusual significance.

*g. Symbols.* The following pages contain the approved symbols for buildings and populated places on large-scale maps.

**Figure 161.   Built-Up Area.**

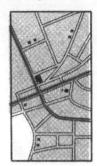 

**Figure 162.   Native settlement.**   Native settlements occur only in foreign areas.   The map legend fully defines the symbol.

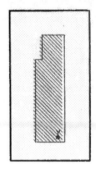 

**Figure 163.   Buildings in General.**

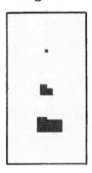 

**Figure 164.   School.**

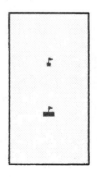 

**Figure 165.    Church.**

**Figure 166.    Christian Shrine.**   A Christian shrine is shown only in foreign areas.   (a) and (b) are alternate symbols, or are sometimes used on the same map to denote different features. Consult the map legend for distinctions.

**Figure 167.    Non-Christian House of Worship.**   A non-Christian house of worship is shown only in foreign areas.   The map legend fully defines the symbol.   (a) and (b) are alternate symbols, or are sometimes used on the same map to denote different features.   Consult the map legend for distinctions.

**Figure 168.    Non-Christian Shrine.**   A non-Christian shrine is shown only in foreign areas.   The map legend fully defines the symbol.   (a), (b), (c), and (d) are alternate symbols, or are sometimes used on the same map to denote different features.   Consult the map legend for distinctions.

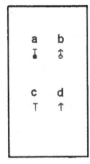

**Figure 169.**    **Mosque.**    A mosque is shown only in foreign areas.

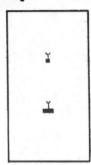 

**Figure 170.**    **Moslem Shrine.**    A Moslem shrine is shown only in foreign areas.    (a) and (b) are alternate symbols, or are sometimes used on the same map to denote different features. Consult the map legend for distinctions:

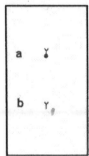 

**Figure 171.**    **Pagoda.**    A pagoda is shown only in foreign areas.

**Figure 172.**    **Structures Similar to Buildings.**

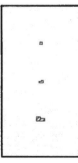 

**Figure 173.   Ruins.**   (a) Large.   (b) Small.

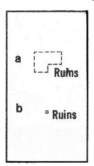

**Figure 174.   Greenhouse.**

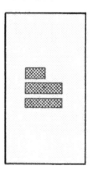

**Figure 175.   Ruined Areas.**

**Figure 176.   Lighthouse or Light.**

**Figure 177.   Windmill or Windpump.**

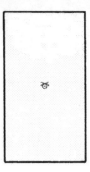

**Figure 178.   Windpump, Alternate Symbol.**

**Figure 179.   Watermill.**

**Figure 180.   Cliff Dwelling.**   Cliff dwellings occur in the southwestern United States.   Where numerous cliff dwellings occur, one symbol is usually used to represent several.

**Figure 181.**   **Historical Site.**   Historical sites are shown only in foreign areas.

**Figure 182.**   **Historical Battlefield.**   Historical battlefields are shown only in foreign areas.

**Figure 183.**   **Cemetery.**   In cemeteries in the United States no distinction is made between denomination or race. In cemeteries in foreign areas, religious denominations are indicated if the information is available. Small private cemeteries and isolated graves are usually omitted.

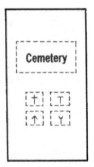 

## 19. BUILDINGS AND POPULATED PLACES ON MEDIUM- AND SMALL-SCALE MAPS

a. Because of the reduced scale, it is impossible to show the buildings and populated places on medium- and small-scale maps in great detail. Consequently, the symbols are truly *symbolic* or representative. The only buildings shown are those which serve as outstanding landmarks in isolated areas.

b. A small populated place is shown by a small circle. A larger populated place is shown, generally true to shape, by an outlined red tinted area. Within the outline, the only features shown are the main-line railroads and through streets.

c. In many areas, there is insufficient informa-tion available to plot the correct outlines of populated places. In such cases, red-filled squares of varying sizes are used as symbols, with the size depending upon the population or importance. Explanations of these squares are contained in the marginal symbol legend of the map.

d. The names of populated places are shown in type of varying sizes, with the size depending upon population or importance. When informa-tion is available, the marginal symbol legend shows the different sizes keyed to a population breakdown. When information is not available, the sizes are keyed to an importance breakdown.

e. *Symbols.* The following pages contain the approved symbol for Buildings and Populated Places on medium- and small-scale maps.

**Figure 184.    Populated Place, Limits Known.**  Size of type used for name indicates population or relative importance.

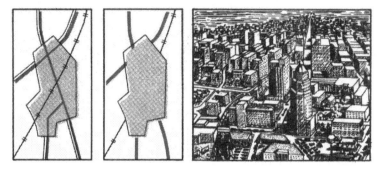

**Figure 185.    Populated Place, Limits Unknown, First Importance.**    Usually a large city or metropolitan area.

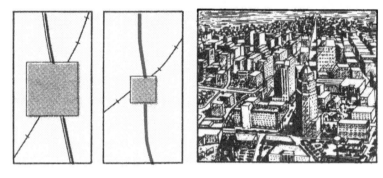

**Figure 186.    Populated Place, Limits Unknown, Second Importance.**    Usually a medium-sized city.

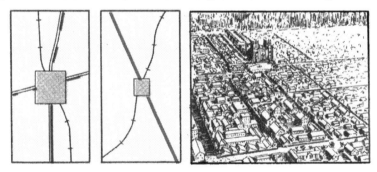

**Figure 187.    Populated Place, Limits Unknown, Third Importance.**    Usually a small city.

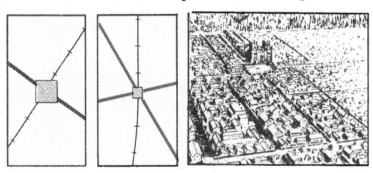

**Figure 188.   Populated Place, Limits Unknown, Fourth Importance.**   Usually a small city or large town.

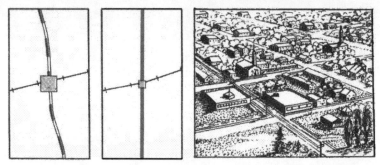

**Figure 189.   Populated Place, Limits Unknown, Fifth Importance.**   Usually a town of fair size.

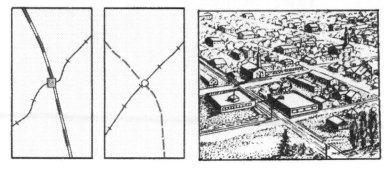

**Figure 190.   Town, Village or Settlement.**

**Figure 191.   Landmark Building.**   Labeling indicates nature or identity of structure.

**Figure 192.   Fort.**

## 20. Industrial and Public Works.

The following symbols indicate the industrial and public works shown at the various scales.

**Figure 193.    Small Dam.**    Includes those dams, either earthen or masonry, too narrow to plot to scale. On certain maps, the symbol in black indicates a masonry dam, and in brown, an earthen dam.

 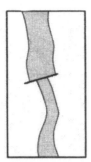      

**Figure 194.    Dam Carrying Road.**    The thickness of the road casings is increased for the length of the dam.

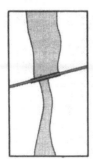 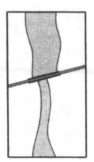      

**Figure 195.    Large Masonry Dam.**    The correct shape of the feature is shown and spillways or other details are included wherever possible.    Buildings located on the dam are shown in their correct position.

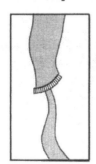 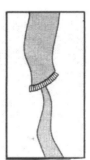      

**Figure 196.    Passable Lock.**    The angle of the symbol always points upstream.

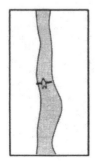

LOCK NOT SHOWN      LOCK NOT SHOWN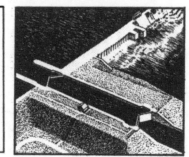

**Figure 197.    Small Canal Lock.**   The angle of the symbol always points upstream.

**Figure 198.    Sluice Gate.**

**Figure 199.    Small Breakwater, Jetty or Diversion Dam.**   Unimportant features are usually omitted.

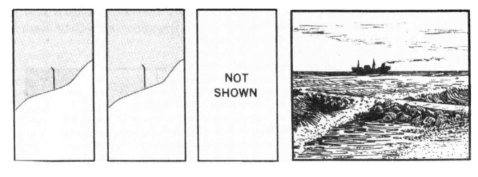

**Figure 200.    Large Breakwater.**

**Figure 201.  Submerged Breakwater.** Breakwaters which are submerged at mean high tide even though exposed at low tide are included.

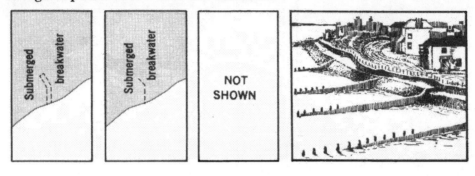

**Figure 202.  Narrow Seawall or Revetment.**

**Figure 203.  Large Seawall.**

**Figure 204.  Large Revetment.**

**Figure 205.　Small Pier, Dock or Wharf.**

**Figure 206.　Large Pier, Dock or Wharf.**

**Figure 207.　Ferry Slip.**

**Figure 208.　Ramp.**　The part submerged at mean high tide is shown by a dashed line.

**Figure 209.   Drydock.**

**Figure 210.   Marine Railroad.**

**Figure 211.   Tank.** Tanks which are used for storage of oil, gas, water, vinegar, or other liquids. Labeling usually describes the contents.

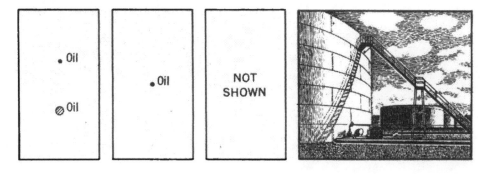

**Figure 212.   Well.** This symbol includes wells drilled for gas, oil, or other minerals, which are in operation. Wells for water are not included. Labeling usually indicates the kind of well.

**Figure 213.   Reservoir, Other Than Water.**  Open reservoirs used for the storage of asphalt, oil, or other liquids except water are indicated if they can be plotted to scale.   Those too small to show to scale are omitted.   Labeling identifies the feature.

**Figure 214.   Sewage Disposal or Filtration Bed.**   These are shown only when they can be plotted to scale.   Wherever possible, major separations within the feature are shown.   Labeling identifies the feature.

**Figure 215.   Swimming Pool.**

**Figure 216.   Pipeline.**   This includes only those pipelines not used for water which are landmark features in areas of sparse culture.   They are omitted in developed areas.   No effort is made to show pipelines as a continuous feature and only landmark parts are shown.

**Figure 217.   Underground Pipeline.**   The symbol represents underground pipelines which are obvious from cleared right of ways, ground scars, or levee-like mounds.

**Figure 218.   Landmark or Located Object.**   A feature is a landmark when it is visible from a distance. Landmarks include towers, chimneys, air beacons, monuments, and similar features. Labeling indicates the nature of the object.

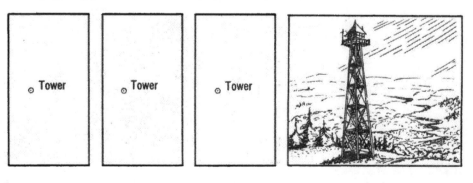

**Figure 219.    Open-Pit Mine or Quarry.** This feature is usually omitted in areas of dense culture.   In foreign areas all types of mines are shown by this symbol, the type of quarry can be indicated by labeling.

**Figure 220.    Mine Shaft.**    A mine shaft is vertical or nearly vertical in direction.    (a) United States.   (b) Foreign.

**Figure 221.    Mine Tunnel.**    A mine tunnel is horizontal or nearly horizontal in direction.    (a) United States.    (b) Foreign.

**Figure 222.    Prospect.**    Prospects are shown only on large-scale maps of the United States.    A prospect is shown only where there is evidence of current or recent digging.

**Figure 223.   Telephone and Telegraph Lines.**   These are shown only when they are landmark features in areas of sparse cultural development.   They are usually omitted along roads or railroads.

**Figure 224.   Power-Transmission Line.**   These are shown only when they are landmark features in areas of sparse cultural development.   They are seldom shown along roads and railroads.   Voltage is not indicated.

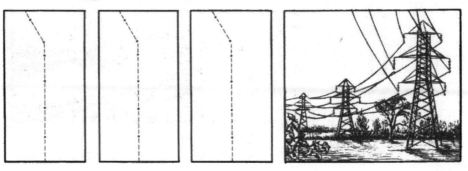

**Figure 225.   Fence, Hedgerow, Field Line.**   This symbol applies to maps of certain foreign areas only.

**Figure 226.   Prominent Fence.**   Only fences which provide definite landmarks in areas of sparse culture are shown.

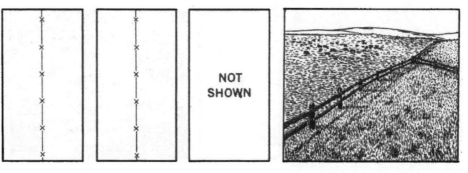

**Figure 227.   Prominent Wall.**   Such walls as the Great Wall of China and walls surrounding forts or cities, and the life are included.   Minor walls are usually not shown.

**Figure 228.   Race Track.**

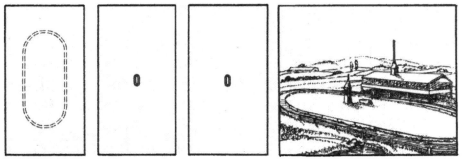

**Figure 229.   Airport or Airfield.**   Airports and airfields are shown to true shape on large-scale maps.

**Figure 230.   Landing Ground.**   Landing grounds are shown to true shape on large-scale maps.

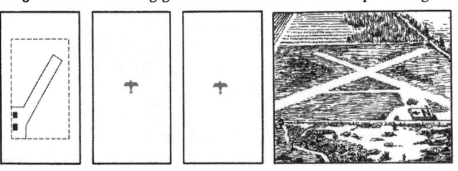

**Figure 231.   Seaplane Base.**   Seaplane bases are shown to true shape on large-scale maps.

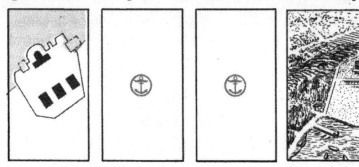

**Figure 232.   Seaplane Anchorage.**   Seaplane anchorages are shown to true shape on large-scale maps.

## 21. CONTROL POINTS AND ELEVATIONS

*a. Application of Definitions.* The definitions of horizontal and vertical control stations which follow are generally applicable only to the United States.

*b. Exceptions.* In foreign areas, horizontal control stations may not be monumented and in some cases may be less than third order accuracy. Whenever information is available, exceptions are noted in the marginal symbol-legend of the map.

*c. Symbols.* The following pages contain the approved symbols for Control Points and Elevations.

**Figure 233.   Horizontal Control Point.**  The symbol represents a described horizontal control point which is marked on the ground and which was established by triangulation or traverse of third or higher order accuracy.

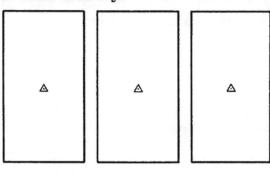

**Figure 234.   Monumented Bench Mark.**  The symbol represents a described vertical control point which is marked by a tablet on the ground and which was established by survey methods of third or higher order accuracy.   (a) and (b) are alternate symbols.

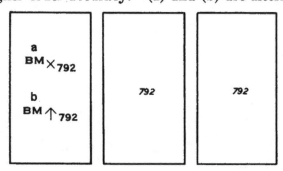

**Figure 235.   Monumented Bench Mark at Horizontal Control Point.**  The symbol represents a described control point which is marked on the ground and whose horizontal and vertical positions were established by survey methods of third or higher order accuracy.

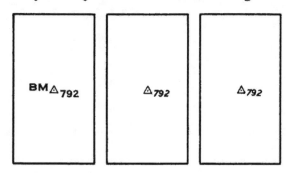

**Figure 236.    Nonmonumented Bench Mark** (sometimes called temporary, supplementary, or intermediate).    The symbol represents a described vertical control point which was established by survey methods of third or higher order accuracy.    The point is usually· recoverable.    The mark does not bear a tablet.

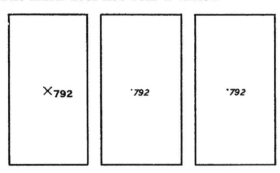

**Figure 237.    Astronomic Position.**    The symbol represents a described horizontal control point whose geographic position was determined through local astronomic observations.

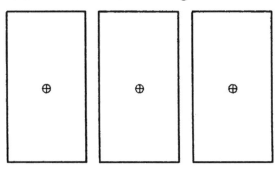

**Figure 238.    Checked Spot Elevation.**    The symbol represents an elevation established by closed lines, including spirit level, stadia, and vertical angle methods.
(a) Identifiable point.    (b) Unidentifiable point.    (c) Unidentifiable point, alternate symbol on large-scale maps.

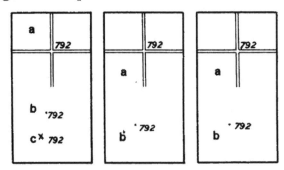

**Figure 239.   Unchecked Spot Elevation.**   The symbol represents an elevation determined by unchecked field surveys such as side shots on stadia lines, unchecked vertical angle or precision altimetry, or by repeated photogrammetric readings.   An unchecked spot elevation is not as reliable as checked spot elevations.

(a) Identifiable point.   (b) Unidentifiable point.   (c) Unidentifiable point, alternate symbol on large-scale maps.

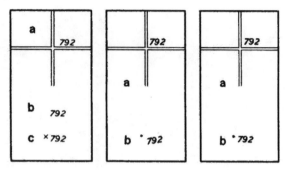

# 22. BOUNDARIES

*a*. Where two or more boundaries coincide, only the symbol representing the higher-ranking boundary is shown.

*b*. Boundaries which are approximate or indefinite are appropriately labeled.

*c*. In cases where a boundary follows a road, small stream, or river, usually only every third unit of the symbol is shown. The intervening symbol units are omitted, except where the omission would create uncertainty as to the alinement of the boundary.

*d*. Terminology of boundaries in foreign areas varies; the map legend contains the correct terms.

*e*. *Symbols*. The following pages contain the approved symbols for Boundaries.

**Figure 240.   International.**

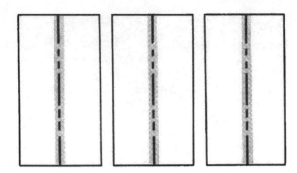

**Figure 241.   Major Administrative.**   (As Intercolonial in French West Africa.)

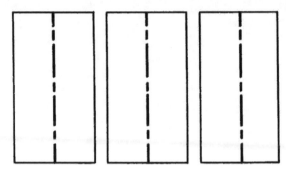

**Figure 242.   First Class Administrative.**   (As State in United States; Province or equivalent in foreign areas.)

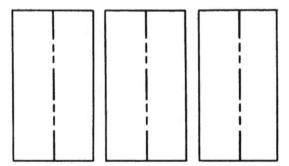

**Figure 243.   Second-Class Administrative.**   (As County or Parish in the United States.)

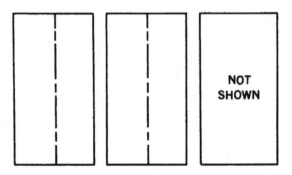

**Figure 244.  Third Class Administrative.**  (As Township in the United States.)

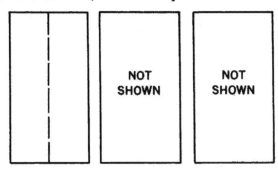

**Figure 245.  Fourth Class Administrative.**  (As Corporate Limits in the United States.)

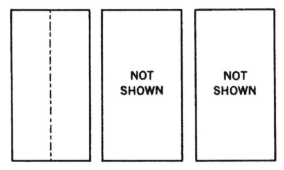

**Figure 246.  Fifth Class Administrative.**  (As Ward in the United States.)  Shown only on very-large-scale maps.

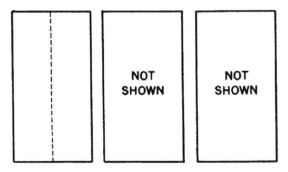

**Figure 247.  Special.**  (As Reservation in the United States.)

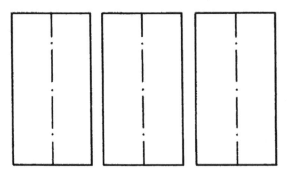

**Figure 248.   International Boundary Marker.**

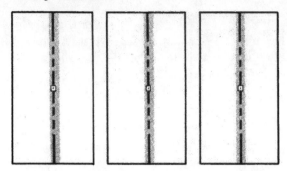

## 23. PUBLIC LAND DATA OF THE UNITED STATES

*a. Application.* Public land data are shown only on large-scale maps of the United States.

*b. Definition.* Public land survey is a rectangular surveying system, instituted by the Federal Government, to divide public lands. The system does not apply to Connecticut, Delaware, Georgia, Kentucky, Maryland, Massachusetts, New Hampshire, New Jersey, New York, North Carolina, Pennsylvania, Rhode Island, South Carolina, Tennessee, Texas, or Virginia. The surveys are not completed in all of the remaining States and are not always continuous throughout a given area.

*c. Primary Lines.* All public land surveys in a given area are referred to two primary lines, a *principal meridian*, and a *base line*, which pass through an initial point. The first is a true north-south line (a meridian) and the other a true east-west line (a parallel) (fig. 249). These two lines are the axes of a system. There are 34 different systems in the United States and Alaska, each with its own principal meridian and base line.

The principal meridian of each is identified by a name or number which is used to reference any subdivision of the system.

*d. Auxiliary Base Lines.* Along the principal meridian at intervals of 24 miles north and south of the base line, auxiliary base lines (true parallels) called *standard parallels* or *correction lines* are extended to the east and west. These lines are numbered with reference to the base line; for example: *second standard parallel north* or *third standard parallel south.*

*e. Guide Meridians.* From the base line and from each standard parallel, *guide meridians* are run due north at intervals of 24 miles east and west of the principal meridian and are terminated at the next standard parallel. These lines are numbered with reference to the principal meridian; for example: *first guide meridian west; second guide meridian east.*

*f. Division Into Areas.* The standard parallels and the guide meridians divide the land into areas exactly 24 miles from north to south, by approximately 24 miles from east to west. The base of the rectangle is exactly 24 miles east to west; the top is 24 miles east to west less convergence.

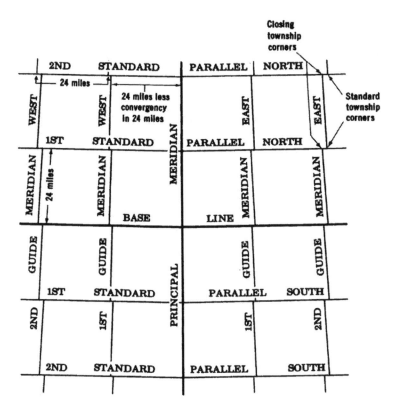

**Figure 249. Standard Land Lines**

*g. Township Divisions.* Each area formed by the standard parallels and guide meridians is further divided into 16 parts (fig. 250), each of which is 6 miles north-south. The base of each part is exactly 6 miles east-west, but the top of each part is 6 miles east-west less convergence. These divisions are called townships. Public-land townships are not the same as and do not necessarily coincide with political townships. The vertical lines dividing the 24-mile rectangle are called *range lines*. These are laid out as true meridians at 6-mile intervals along each standard parallel and extended due north to the next standard parallel. The horizontal lines which divide the 24-mile rectangle are called *township lines*. These are laid out as true parallels at 6-mile intervals along the principal and guide meridians.

*h. Township Designations.* The rows, each 6 miles north-south, formed by the township lines are numbered from the base line, as: T1N, T2N, T3N, and so on, and T1S, T2S, T3S, and so on. These are called *township rows*. The columns, each 6 miles east-west, formed by the range lines are numbered from the principal meridian, as: R1W, R2W, R3W, and so on, and R1E, R2E, R3E, and so on. These are called *ranges*. Each township is designated by its township and range numbers, followed by its principal meridian, as, for example: T5N, R6W, Fourth Principal Meridian.

*i. Sections.* Each township is subdivided into 36 sections. The sections are formed by straight lines, 1 mile apart, running parallel to the eastern range line, and by straight lines, 1 mile apart,

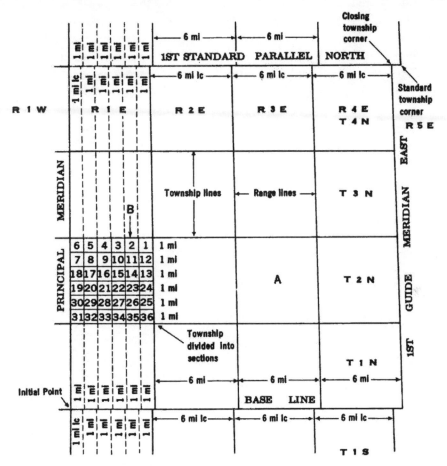

NOTE: Distances shown are theoretical; no errors in surveying are shown.
The abbreviation lc indicates "less convergence".

Examples of designations:
A—Township, T2N, R3E, plus name of principal meridian.
B—Section 2, T2N, R1E, plus name of principal meridian.

**Figure 250. Townships and Sections.**

running parallel to the south township line. These lines are referred to as *section lines*. Since the eastern and western boundaries of sections run parallel to the east boundary of the township, it follows that if the surveys are without error, all sections except those adjacent to the west boundary will be 1 mile square. Those adjacent to the west boundary will have an east-west dimension less than 1 mile by an amount equal to the convergency of the range lines. In addition to the convergency, accumulated errors in surveying are encountered. These errors, by legal ruling, are not distributed along section lines but are all grouped in the western column and in the northern row of sections in each township.

*j. Numbering of Sections.* Sections are numbered consecutively from east to west and west to east, beginning with number 1 in the northeast corner of the township, and ending with number 36 in the southeast corner (fig 250). The legal designation of a section is written as, for example: Section 15, T5N, R6W, Fourth Principal Meridian.

*k. Further Subdivisions.* For reference purposes, sections are further subdivided into ½, ¼, ⅛, and ⅟₁₆ sections. Discussion of these is omitted from this manual since they are not shown on standard topographic maps.

*l. Land Grants.* Territories acquired by the Federal Government became public lands except where title to tracts of land had previously been granted to individuals, groups, or institutions. These areas, frequently irregular in shape, are referred to as *land grants*, or simply *grants*, and are usually identified by a name or number.

*m. Corners.* In making the original public land survey, each intersection of land lines was marked by a monument. These are referred to as *corners*. Corners consist of two basic types—standard corners and closing corners (fig. 250). A standard corner is established by east or west surveys along base lines or standard parallels. Theoretically, these corners are 24 miles apart. A closing corner is established on a base line or standard parallel by intersection with a meridian extended north from a standard corner on the south. These corners are spaced at intervals of less than 24 miles due to convergence of the meridians. The only corners symbolized on the map are either *true* or *accepted* corners. A true corner is one which has been definitely recovered in the field. An accepted corner is one for which acceptable evidence exists as to its location although the monument has not been recovered.

*n. Symbols.* The following pages contain the approved symbols for Public Land Data of the United States.

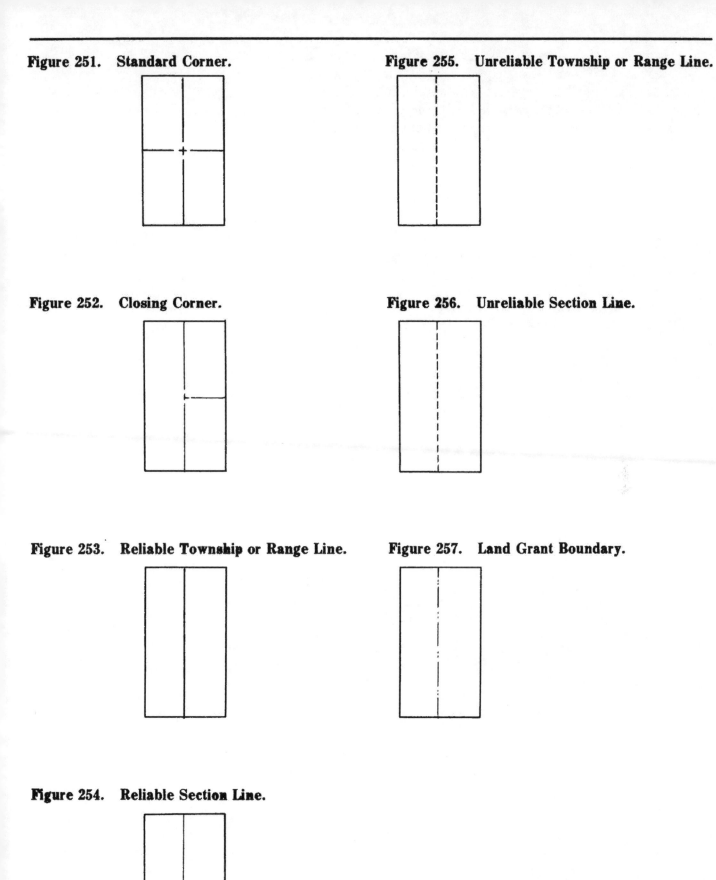

Figure 251.   Standard Corner.

Figure 255.   Unreliable Township or Range Line.

Figure 252.   Closing Corner.

Figure 256.   Unreliable Section Line.

Figure 253.   Reliable Township or Range Line.

Figure 257.   Land Grant Boundary.

Figure 254.   Reliable Section Line.

# CHAPTER 3

## TOPOGRAPHIC ABBREVIATIONS

### 24. SCOPE

Appendix II contains the list of topographic abbreviations authorized for use on the standard topographic maps discussed in this manual.

### 25. APPLICATION

*a.* Abbreviations on the face of the map are held to an absolute minimum They are employed only where space prohibits the use of a full term or where use of the full term would require unreasonable repetition.

*b.* Periods are omitted from abbreviations on the face of the map.

*c.* In the margin, periods are normally retained. They are, however, omitted from coded abbreviations of governmental agency names. In such cases, no spacing is shown between the coded letters.

*d.* In addition to the abbreviations listed herein, commonly accepted abbreviations of time, measures and countries are authorized.

### 26. LIST OF ABBREVIATIONS, AND THEIR MEANINGS

Appendix II contains an alphabetical list of authorized topographic abbreviations and their meanings.

# CHAPTER 4
# MARGINAL INFORMATION

## 27. SCOPE

*a.* This chapter explains the map identifications and other marginal data appearing on topographic maps prepared for use by the Department of the Army.

*b.* These marginal items are illustrated in the charts which are in appendix III. They are—

Chart 1—large-scale maps.
Chart 2—medium-scale maps.
Chart 3—small-scale maps.

*c.* The arrangement of marginal items will vary; for example, on sheets having a narrow east-west neatline dimension, certain items will appear in the right-hand margin rather than in the lower margin. The composition is generally the same for maps at like scales.

*d.* Detailed information on marginal data will be found in AMS technical manuals published under the direction of the Chief of Engineers.

## 28. MAP IDENTIFICATIONS

*a. General.* Map identifications are those items appearing in the margins of maps which serve to identify any individual map completely. On maps prepared for the Department of the Army these identifications are the series name, the series number and scale, the edition number, the sheet name and sheet number, the unit imprint with key number and the geographic location name.

*b. Series Name.* A series, which normally consists of maps of a common scale which collectively cover a specific area, is generally assigned the geographical or the political name of the area covered.

*c. Series Number.* The series number is a comprehensive reference composed of four elements, either four numerals or a letter and three numerals. The number is unique for the series. It identifies the area and scale of the series.

*d. Series Scale.* The scale is written as a ratio of map distance to ground distance.

*e. Edition Number.* The edition number is a specific identification based on the publication sequence of a particular map. Edition numbers run consecutively; thus, it can be assumed that a map labeled with a higher edition number contains more recent information than another printing of the same map labeled with a lower edition number.

*f. Sheet Name.* Generally, a map is named after its outstanding cultural or geographic feature. The name of a cultural feature is customarily chosen, but if a geographic feature is better known than any cultural feature appearing on the map, the geographic feature name is chosen.

*g. Sheet Number.* Sheet numbers for large-scale maps are based on an arbitrary geographic coordinate system covering the area to be mapped. The sheet number of a 1:25,000 scale sheet is directly related to the number of a 1:50,000 scale sheet covering the same area. Sheet numbers for medium- and small-scale maps are based on the International Map of the World (IMW) numbering system.

*h. Unit Imprint and Key Number.* The unit imprint proper is the signature of the agency responsible for printing the map. This is followed by the printing date identifying the particular printing, and finally the key number which is a unique number assigned to each individual map to facilitate filing and ordering.

*i. Geographic-Location Name.* The geographic-location name indicates the country, state, or general geographic area within which the map lies. The geographic-location name is preceded by the sheet name, which is repeated in the lower margin. Large-scale maps of the United States which cover an area entirely within one county or parish, carry the county or parish name below the sheet name-geographic location name.

## 29. OTHER MARGINAL DATA

a. *General.* In addition to the identifications described above, the margin of the map contains other information important to the map user in evaluating and interpreting the map (table I).

TABLE I. *Other Marginal Data*

| Marginal data | Large scale | Medium scale | Small scale |
|---|---|---|---|
| Bar scales | Yes | Yes | Yes |
| Contour interval note, or Altitude Tint Legend | Yes | Yes | Yes |
| Coverage diagram | Yes | No | No |
| Credit of sources note | Yes | Yes | Yes |
| Glossary (in foreign areas when native language is other than English) | Yes | Yes | Yes |
| Grid notes and information | Yes | Yes | No |
| Horizontal datum-plane note | Yes | Yes | Yes |
| Hydrographic datum notes | Yes | No* | No |
| Index to adjoining sheets (or location diagram) | Yes | Yes | Yes |
| Index to the boundaries diagram, or Location Index | Yes | Yes | Yes |
| Magnetic declination note | Yes | Yes | No |
| Projection note | Yes | Yes | Yes |
| Reliability diagram | No | Yes | Yes |
| Security classification when required | Yes | Yes | Yes |
| Symbol legend | Yes | Yes | Yes |
| Users note (concerning corrections) | Yes | Yes | Yes |
| Vertical datum note | Yes | Yes | Yes |

(1) When required, special notes referring to items within the map are placed in the lower margin.

(2) Coverage diagrams and hydrographic datum notes are sometimes shown on 1:100,000 maps for tactical use.

b. *Credit Note.* The credit note aids in evaluating the map and contains interpretive information. The note describes the method of preparation, identifies the source material used in compilation, gives the dates of aerial photography, lists the source of horizontal and vertical control, and notes the origin of reference of public land lines. It notes whether the map conforms with national map accuracy requirements and whether the map has been field checked. It includes any special information pertinent to the particular sheet.

c. *Symbol Legend.* The symbol legend defines and illustrates the symbols most commonly used, as populated places, roads, railroads, etc. It also contains symbols for items peculiar to the area being mapped.

d. *Index to Adjoining Sheets.* The index to adjoining sheets, or on 1:250,000 scale maps, the location diagram, identifies the sheets surrounding the sheet under consideration.

e. *Index to Boundaries.* The index to boundaries identifies the political areas appearing in the body of the map. The boundaries in the diagram are schematic but serve as aids in locating the boundaries on the map. On the 1:250,000 scale maps this information is shown in the location diagram.

f. *Coverage Diagram.* The coverage diagram, shown on large-scale maps, portrays in graphic form the methods of compilation, notes the dates of any photography used, and identifies and evaluates any maps used as bases.

g. *Reliability Diagram.* The reliability diagram, shown on medium- and small-scale maps, contains graphic references to the reliability of the sources used and identifies the scale, method of survey and date of the basic sources.

h. *Datum Notes.* The horizontal, vertical, and hydrographic datum notes identify the controls used for these items on the map. Generally, horizontal and hydrographic datum notes are not shown on medium- and small-scale maps.

i. *Grid Notes and Data.* Maps of 1:250,000 and larger scale contain grid notes and a grid reference box with sample reference, explaining the grid data on the map. Maps carrying a 1,000 unit grid also show a declination diagram and a protractor scale in the margin. The declination diagram shows the relationship between true north, magnetic north and grid north for the major grid at the center of the sheet. Maps carrying a 10,000 unit grid show a magnetic declination note. This note indicates the variation in the magnetic declination between the centers of the east and west map edges. It also shows the mean annual change.

# APPENDIX I

# REFERENCES

## 1. DEPARTMENT OF THE ARMY PUBLICATIONS

### a. Regulations.

#### (1) Army Regulations.

AR 10–260　　Corps of Engineers.

AR 300–15　　Mapping and Charting.

AR 310–30　　Organization and Equipment Authorization Tables.

AR 320–50　　Military Terms, Abbreviations and Symbols.

#### (2) Special Regulations.

SR 10–5–1　　Organization and Functions, Department of the Army.

SR 110–1–1　　Index of Army Motion Pictures and Film Strips, and Kinescope Recordings.

SR 135–310–1　　Civilian Components, Training Material.

SR 310–5–1　　Military Publications, Procurement and Production.

SR 310–20–1　　Military Publications, Numbering of Department of the Army Publications.

SR 310–20–3　　Index of Army Training Publications.

SR 310–20–4　　Index of Technical Manuals, Technical Bulletins, Supply Bulletins, Lubrication Orders, Modification Work Orders, Tables of Organization and Equipment, Reduction Tables, Tables of Allowances, Tables of Organization, and Tables of Equipment.

SR 310–20–5　　Index of Administrative Publications.

SR 310–30–1　　Organization and Equipment Authorization Tables.

SR 320–5–1　　Dictionary of United States Army Terms.

SR 320–50–1　　Authorized Abbreviations.

### b. Field Manuals.

FM 5–5　　Engineer Troops.

FM 21–8　　Military Training Aids.

FM 21–25　　Elementary Map and Aerial Photograph Reading.

FM 21–26　　Advanced Map and Aerial Photograph Reading.

FM 21–30　　Military Symbols.

FM 30–5　　Military Intelligence—Combat Intelligence.

FM 30–20　　Military Intelligence—Military Maps.

FM 30–21　　Aerial Photography, Military Aplications.

FM 30–22　　Military Intelligence—Foreign Conventional Signs and Symbols.

FM 101–10　　Staff Officers' Field Manual: Organization, Technical, and Logistical Data.

### c. Technical Manuals.

FM 5–230　　Topographic Drafting.

FM 5–240　　Aerial Phototopography.

FM 5–244　　Multiplex Mapping Equipment.

FM 5–245　　Map Reproduction in the Field.

FM 5–246　　Interpretation of Aerial Photographs.

TM 5–248　　Foreign Maps.

TM 5–9990　　Kit Instruction Map Reading.

TM 12–250　　Administration.

### d. Tables of Organization and Equipment.

T/O & E 5–55　　Engineer Topographic Battalion, Army.

T/O & E 5–56　　Headquarters, Headquarters and Service Company, Engineer Topographic Battalion, Army.

T/O & E 5–57　　Engineer Map Reproduction and Distribution Company, Army.

T/O & E 5–59　　Engineer Photomapping Company Army.

T/O & E 5–167 Engineer Topographic Company, Corps.

T/O & E 5–184 Engineer Base Map Distribution Company, Engineer Base Topographic Battalion.

T/O & E 5–186 Headquarters and Headquarters Company, Engineer Base Topographic Battalion.

T/O & E 5–347 Engineer Base Reproduction Company.

T/O & E 5–348 Engineer Base Survey Company (and Change 1 to Appendix I, Arctic Operations).

T/O & E 5–349 Engineer Base Photomapping Company.

T/O & E 5–500 Engineer Service Organizations.
    IA Engineer Topographic Staff Team.
    IB Engineer Survey Team.
    IC Engineer Survey Platoon.
    ID Engineer Photomapping Platoon.
    IE Engineer Reproduction Platoon.
    IF Engineer Map Distribution Platoon.
    IG Engineer Relief Map Making Team.
    IH Engineer Relief Map Making Platoon.
    IN Engineer Hydrology Team.
    IP Engineer Geodetic Survey Team.

*c. Graphic Training Aids.*

GTA 5–2     Elementary Map Reading.

GTA 5–12    Coordinate Scales and Protractors.

*f. Films and Film Strips.*
    Map reading:
      Basic:

TF 21–2071    Conventional signs.

TF 21–2072    Elevation, distance, and grid.

TF 21–2073    Direction, orientation and location with compass.

TF 21–2074    Direction, orientation, and location without compass.

TF 21–2075    Photos and photomaps.

TF 5–1270    British conventional signs and symbols.

TF 5–12     Map reading.

TF 11–556    Motor vehicle driver—Map reading.

FS 1–2102    Fundamentals of aerial map reading.

*g. Supply Catalogs (Sets of Equipment).*

ENG 6

390–01    Computing and drafting equipment, Set No. 1.

*Drafting Equipment*

430–01    Set No. 1, Battalion.
430–02    Set No. 2, Company.
430–03    Set No. 3, Regiment.
430–04    Set No. 4, CAC Battalion.
430–05    Set No. 5, CAC Battery.
430–06    Set No. 6, CAC Harbor Defense.
430–07    Set No. 7, CAC Regiment.
430–08    Set No. 8, FA Flash Ranging.
430–09    Set No. 9, FA Sound Ranging.
430–10    Set No. 10, Topographic Battalion, Headquarters and Service Company.
430–11    Set No. 11, Topographic Battalion, Photomapping Company.
430–12    Set No. 12, Topographic Battalion, Reproduction Company.
440–01    Drafting and Duplicating Equipment, Set No. 1.

*Instrument Drawing*

515–01    Field set.
515–02    Office set.
515–03    Pocket set.

*Instruments, Plotting, Stereoscopic, Multiplex*

520–01    Set No. 1, Control Booth.
520–02    Set No. 2, Drafting Unit.
520–03    Set No. 3, Laboratory.
520–04    Set No. 4, Plotting Booth.
520–05    Set No. 5, Repair.
520–06    Set No. 6, Supplementary.

*Library References*

570–07    Set No. 7, Topographic Battalion, Headquarters Service Company, Army.
570–08    Set No. 8, Topographic Battalion, Headquarters Service Company GHQ.
570–09    Set No. 9, Topographic Battalion, Photomapping Company.
570–10    Set No. 10, Topographic Battalion, Reproduction Company.
570–11    Set No. 11, Topographic Battalion, Survey Company.

570–12    Set No. 12, Topographic Company, Aviation.

570–13    Set No. 13, Topographic Company, Corps.

### *Map Distribution Equipment*

580–01    Set No. 1.

580–02    Set No. 2.

### *Photomapping Equipment*

630–01    Set No. 1, Topographic Battalion, Army.

630–02    Set No. 2, Topographic Company, Aviation.

630–03    Set No. 3, Topographic Company, Corps.

670–01    Power Plant, Trailer Mounted, 5–KW.

700–01    Repair Equipment, Set No. 1, Instrument, Topographic Battalion.

### *Reproduction Equipment*

710–01    Set No. 1, Ammonia Process.

710–02    Set No. 2, Black and White Process.

710–03    Set No. 3, Gelatin Process 18 x 18 Inches.

710–04    Set No. 4, Gelatin Process 22 x 23 Inches.

710–05    Set No. 5, Portable for Task Force.

### *Reproduction Equipment, Topographic*

720–01    Set No. 1, Lithographic Platoon, Topographic Battalion HQ.

721–02    Set No. 2, 24 x 24 in., mounted on a 4-ton 6 x 6 standard truck chassis with van type body.

721–06    Set No. 6, 24 x 30, mounted on a 4-ton 6 x 6 standard truck chassis with van type body.

735–01    Reproduction Kit, Set No. 1, Sign. Silk Screen Process.

830–01    Sign Painting Equipment, Set No. 1.

840–01    Sketching Equipment, Set No. 1.

860–01    Stereocomparagraph Equipment, Set No. 1.

870–15    Supplementary Equipment, Set No. 15, Survey Company, Topographic Battalion.

## 2. DEPARTMENT OF COMMERCE PUBLICATIONS

*a. U. S. Coast and Geodetic Survey Special Publications.*

| No. | Nomenclature |
| --- | --- |
| 8 | Tables and Formulas for the Computation of Geodetic Positions. |
| 28 | Application of the Theory of Least Squares to the Adjustment of Triangulations. |
| 60 | A Study of Map Projection in General. |
| 68 | Elements of Map Projection. |
| 144 | Topographic Manual. |
| 193 | Manual of Plane Coordinate Computation. |
| 195 | Manual of Traverse Computation on the Transverse Mercator Grid. |
| 200 | Formulas and Tables for the Computation of Geodetic Positions on the International Ellipsoid. |
| 205 | Cartography. |
| 241 | Natural Tables for the Computation of Geodetic Positions. |
| 242 | Definitions of Terms used in Geodetic and Other Surveys. |

*b. U. S. Coast and Geodetic Survey Serials.*

583    Control Survey and Their Uses.

584    Azimuths from Plane Coordinates.

## 3. DEPARTMENT OF INTERIOR PUBLICATIONS

*U. S. Geological Survey Bulletins*

788    Topographical Instructions.

# APPENDIX II

## TOPOGRAPHIC ABBREVIATIONS

| | | | |
|---|---|---|---|
| A | Army | Colo | Colorado |
| Aband | abandoned | Comm | Commission |
| AF | Air Force | Conn | Connecticut |
| AFB | Air Force Base | Const | construction |
| Ala | Alabama | CR | crossroads |
| Align | alignment | Cr | creek |
| Alt | Alternate | Cus Ho | customhouse |
| AMS | Army Map Service | | |
| Anc | ancient | DC | District of Columbia. |
| Anch | anchorage | Dec | December. |
| Approx | approximate | Deg | degrees. |
| Apr | April | Del | Delaware. |
| Arch | archipelago | Dept | department. |
| Ariz | Arizona | Div | division. |
| Ark | Arkansas | DSvy | Directorate of Military Surveys (Great Britain). |
| ASE | Army Survey Establishment (Canada) | | |
| Aug | August | E | east. |
| Ave | Avenue | Elec | electric, electrified. |
| | | Elev | elevated. |
| B | bay | Fd | ford. |
| Bdry | boundary | Feb | February. |
| Bk | brook | Fl | flood. |
| Bldg | building | Fla | Florida. |
| Blvd | boulevard. | Fld | field. |
| BM | benchmark. | Fm | fathom. |
| Br | branch | For | forest. |
| Brg | bridge | Ft | fort. |
| Byp | bypass | Fy | ferry. |
| C | cape | G | gulf. |
| Calif | California. | Ga | Georgia. |
| Cath | cathedral | Gas | gasoline. |
| CE | Corps of Engineers. | GN | grid north. |
| Cem | cemetery | Govt | government. |
| CG | Coast Guard | Grd | ground. |
| CH | courthouse | GSGS | Geographic Section, General Staff (Great Britain). |
| Ch | church | | |
| Chan | channel | Hbr | harbor. |
| Chy | chimney | Hosp | hospital. |
| Co | county | HS | high school. |
| Col | college | Hy | highway. |

| | |
|---|---|
| I | island. |
| Ill | Illinois. |
| In | inlet. |
| Ind | Indiana. |
| Jan | January. |
| Jul | July. |
| Jun | June. |
| Junc | junction. |
| Kans | Kansas. |
| Km | kilometer. |
| Kn | knot. |
| Ky | Kentucky. |
| L | lake. |
| La | Louisiana. |
| Lat | latitude. |
| Ldg | landing. |
| LH | lighthouse. |
| Long | longitude. |
| M | meter(s). |
| Mag | magnetic. |
| Mar | March. |
| Mass | Massachusetts. |
| Md | Maryland. |
| Mi | mile(s). |
| Mich | Michigan. |
| Mil | military. |
| Min | minute(s). |
| Minn | Minnesota. |
| Miss | Mississippi. |
| Mo | Missouri. |
| Mon | monument. |
| Mont | Montana. |
| Mt | mount, mountain. |
| Mts | mountains. |
| N | north. |
| Natl | national. |
| Nav | navigable. |
| NC | North Carolina. |
| N Dak | North Dakota. |
| Nebr | Nebraska. |
| Nev | Nevada. |
| NH | New Hampshire. |
| NJ | New Jersey. |
| N Mex | New Mexico. |
| No | number. |
| Nov | November. |
| NY | New York. |
| Obs | obstacle. |
| Obstr | obstruction. |
| Oct | October. |

| | |
|---|---|
| Okla | Oklahoma. |
| Oreg | Oregon. |
| P | Post office. |
| P | protractor point (pivot point). |
| Pa | Pennsylvania. |
| Pen, Pena | peninsula. |
| Pk | peak. |
| Pky | parkway. |
| PO | post office. |
| Pt | point. |
| PT | post and telegraph office. |
| Quar | quarantine. |
| R | range (public lands). |
| Rd | road. |
| Res | reservation. |
| Res | reservoir. |
| RI | Rhode Island. |
| RR | railroad. |
| RS | radio station. |
| Ry | railway. |
| S | south. |
| SC | South Carolina. |
| Sch | school. |
| S Dak | South Dakota. |
| sec | second (s). |
| Sept | September. |
| St | Saint. |
| St | street. |
| Sta | station. |
| Ste | Sainte. |
| Str | stream. |
| Subm | submerged. |
| T | telegraph office. |
| T | township tier (public lands). |
| Tel | telephone or telegraph line. |
| Temp | temporary. |
| Tenn | Tennessee. |
| Tex | Texas. |
| Tnpk | turnpike. |
| Tr | tower. |
| Univ | university. |
| US | United States. |
| USC&GS | United States Coast and Geodetic Survey. |
| USDA | United States Department of Agriculture. |
| USFS | United States Forest Service. |
| USGS | United States Geological Survey. |

| | |
|---|---|
| USHO | United States Hydrographic Office. |
| USLS | United States Lake Survey. |
| Va | Virginia. |
| VABM | vertical angle bench mark. |
| Vil | village. |
| Vt | Vermont. |
| W | west. |

| | |
|---|---|
| Wash | Washington. |
| Wdm | windmill. |
| Wis | Wisconsin. |
| WM | water mill. |
| WT | water tank, water tower. |
| W Va | West Virginia. |
| Wyo | Wyoming. |
| Yd | yard. |
| Yds | yards. |

# APPENDIX III

# CHARTS

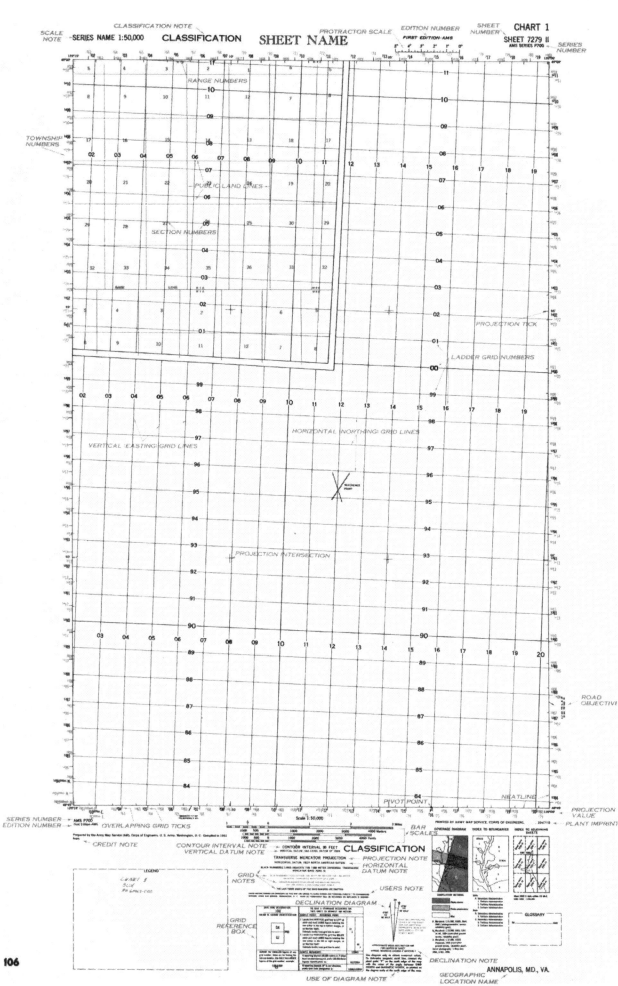

CHART 1

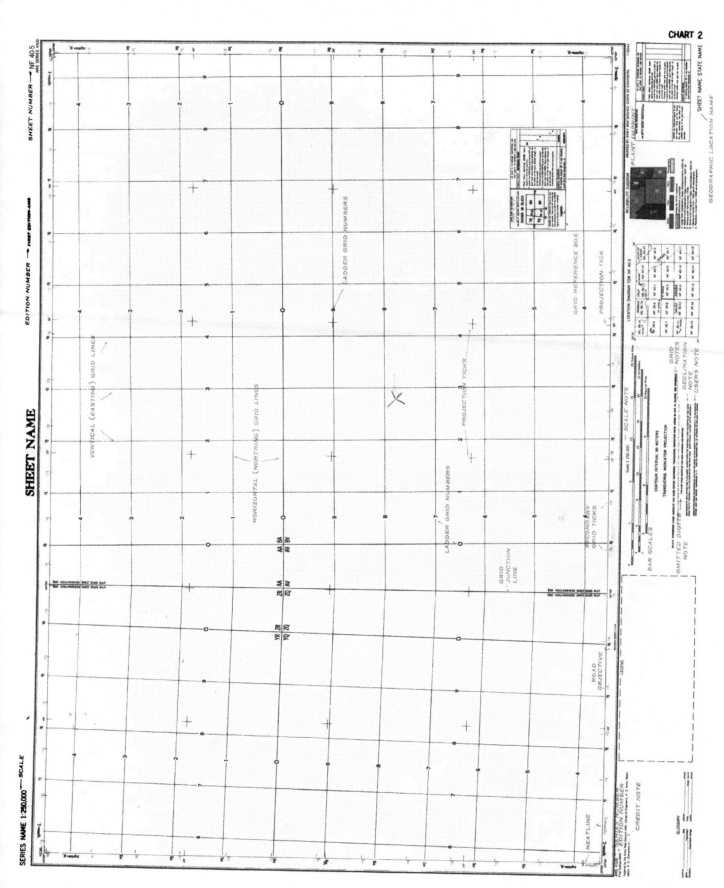

CHART 2

107

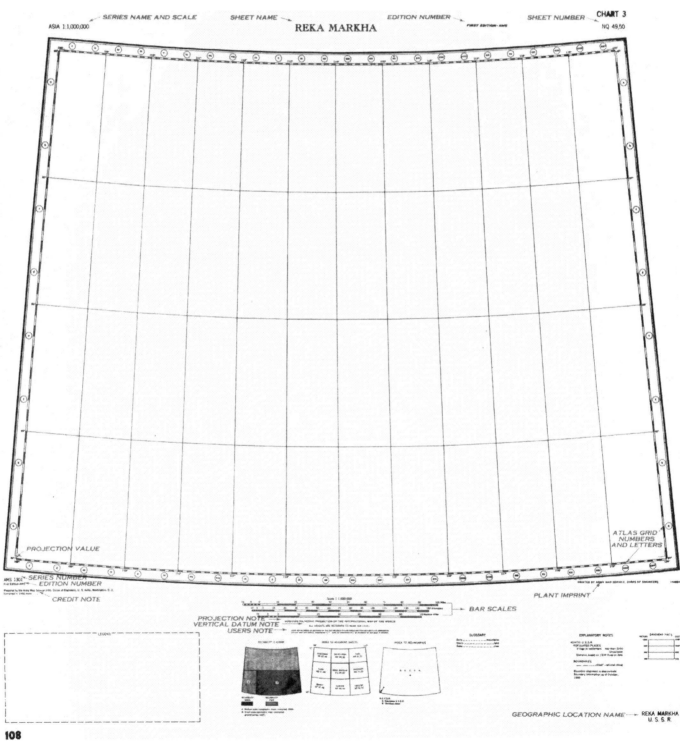

# INDEX

21723874R00072